THE FRENCH DRAWINGS
AT WINDSOR CASTLE

PHAIDON PRESS

1945

APOLLON.   LE ROY.

HENRI GISSEY: Louis XIV as Apollo. *Design for a ballet.* Catalogue No. 72

THE FRENCH DRAWINGS

IN THE COLLECTION OF

HIS MAJESTY THE KING

AT WINDSOR CASTLE

BY

ANTHONY BLUNT

SURVEYOR OF THE KING'S PICTURES

1945

OXFORD & LONDON: PHAIDON PRESS LTD
NEW YORK: OXFORD UNIVERSITY PRESS

PRINTED IN ENGLAND AT THE CURWEN PRESS

INTRODUCTION

THE series of drawings of the French school in the Royal Library at Windsor is in many respects unique. In size it does not compare with the collection of the same school in the Louvre, nor probably even with that in the Hermitage; but in certain respects it is richer than either of these. Nowhere in the world is it possible to see a group of drawings by Nicolas Poussin, the greatest of all French classical draughtsmen, comparable in quality, range, preservation and associative interest with those at Windsor; and with the exception of the splendid series in the British Museum, the work of his great contemporary in landscape, Claude Gellée, is perhaps more beautifully represented in the Royal Library than in any other collection.

On the other hand in certain periods and styles the Windsor collection is remarkably weak. The sixteenth century is poorly represented; there are hardly any examples of the great draughtsmen of the eighteenth century, and the nineteenth century is to all intents and purposes limited to a series of official water-colours illustrating events connected with the life of the Court, none of which is by an artist of the first rank.

Both the strength and the weakness of the collection can be accounted for by the manner in which it was formed. If we ignore for the moment the nineteenth-century drawings, the greater part was acquired by two collectors, Frederick Prince of Wales and his son, George III. Naturally their choice was governed by the official English taste of the period, which is best defined in the *Discourses* of Sir Joshua Reynolds. For him European art consisted of the classical tradition as it was founded by Raphael and Michelangelo—both nobly represented at Windsor—revived by the Carracci at the beginning of the seventeenth century, and carried on by certain members of the Roman school of the next generations. The work of these artists—Domenichino, Andrea Sacchi and Carlo Maratta, together with Guido Reni, and Guercino, who continued the tradition of the Carracci in Bologna—bulks largest in the Royal Library, and indeed fills half of the shelves devoted to the Italian school. With this group of painters are closely associated the two most purely classical artists of the time, French by birth but Roman by adoption, namely Poussin and Claude, the former of whom was regarded by Reynolds as almost the equal of the great Renaissance masters. It is therefore natural that the two founders of the Royal collection should have paid particular attention to the acquisition of works by these artists.

The same rigid taste accounts for the gaps in the French drawings at Windsor. To Reynolds and his contemporaries the work of sixteenth-century French artists would have seemed 'Gothic', and it could have had at most a purely historical significance. It was no doubt this interest that led to the acquisition of the portrait drawings representing ladies and gentlemen of the court of France which form more than half of the sixteenth-century section. In the same way French art of the eighteenth century had little to offer to those who thought like Reynolds. The Rococo was too frivolous, and the naturalism of painters like Chardin lacked idealism and classicism. It is therefore natural that the drawings of this period at Windsor should be somewhat insignificant, and most of them have some non-æsthetic interest, e.g. the portraits of royal personages, or the Parrocel drawings for a treatise on riding. The only two French eighteenth-century drawings of real quality in the whole collection are the Boucher design for the frontispiece to Julienne's volume of engravings after Watteau, a splendid sketch in the pure Rococo manner, and a small drawing by Watteau of a man wearing a turban.

English taste in the eighteenth century also accounts for another curious fact about the French drawings at Windsor, namely that they were almost all bought in Italy. Although Paris in the middle of the eighteenth century was an important centre of the art market, it was in general too much dominated by Rococo taste to have much to offer to those who were buying for the Royal collection. Rome was the centre of the tradition which they principally admired; and, moreover, the great Roman families had almost all fallen on evil days and were ready to part with their treasures in the face of the tempting offers of the rich English travellers.

It was therefore natural that the agents of the Royal collectors should make Rome their principal field; but this fact affected the type of drawing which they acquired when it came to the French school. By far the greater part of the French drawings at Windsor are by artists who were in one way or another connected with Italy. As has already been said, the two draughtsmen most brilliantly represented in the Royal Library are Poussin and Claude. Of other artists in whose work the collection is rich, Callot worked for many years in Florence, Gaspard Dughet lived in Rome, and La Fage visited Italy where he probably executed the drawings now at Windsor. In certain instances this strong Roman emphasis produces results of interest, as for example in the case of a signed landscape drawing by Charles Simonneau, which clearly depicts an Italian scene, whereas it was not otherwise known that this artist ever went to Italy. There are, it is true, also drawings by artists like Le Sueur and La Hyre who never left France, but they are the exception.

*   *   *   *   *

Some indication has been given of the scope of the French drawings in the Royal Library, but it will be worth while considering in greater detail the works of the two artists in which the collection is conspicuously rich, namely Poussin and Claude.

There are 133 drawings connected with the name of Poussin at Windsor, of which 68 can be regarded as unquestionably from his own hand, and almost all the rest as produced under his direction in his studio or else by close followers. The exact history of these drawings is discussed in the following catalogue, and here it will be enough to say that they come in the main from the artist's three best Italian patrons, the Cavaliere Marino, the Cavaliere Cassiano del Pozzo and Cardinal Camillo Massimi. The first was the king of Mannerist poets, who 'discovered' Poussin on his visit to Paris between 1615 and 1623, and ordered from him, as one of his earliest commissions, the series of drawings illustrating Ovid, now in the Royal Library. Marino died in 1625, a year after Poussin arrived in Rome at his invitation, but he had already introduced the artist to intellectual circles in Rome, in particular to Cardinal Francesco Barberini. The cardinal was a good patron of the arts, but by far the greatest benefit which Poussin derived from this introduction was that it brought him into contact with Cassiano del Pozzo, who was secretary to the cardinal. Cassiano, who was to become Poussin's main support for the next fifteen years, is a singularly attractive character. As a lawyer of distinction and secretary to the nephew of the Pope, Urban VIII, he occupied a position of considerable importance; but he seems never to have sought prominence, and to have deliberately preferred a life of relative retirement in which he could indulge his real passion, the study of antiquity. To further this pursuit he gathered round him a group of artists whom he commissioned to make drawings of all the remains of ancient painting and sculpture in Rome. This collection is now to be found in a series of volumes in the Royal Library, to which they came with the Albani drawings. Curiously enough, though Poussin is known to have made drawings after antiquities for Cassiano, there is not a single one in the volumes at Windsor which can be attributed to him, though a few in the main collection may originally have come from them. There are, however, many drawings of mythological and religious subjects by him which certainly belonged to Cassiano and were probably executed specially for him.

Poussin's third Italian patron, Cardinal Massimi, is a man of rather the same type. After pursuing a career of some distinction as a diplomat of the papal court he fell out of favour, but as his public activities grew less he seized the opportunity of pursuing his private interests, which were the same as those of Cassiano. He too was a keen student of antiquity, and he carried on the work of Cassiano in recording the remains of ancient Rome. Some of his archæological volumes are also at Windsor, acquired, as was probably also his volume of Poussin drawings, by Frederick Prince of Wales from Dr. Mead in the first half of the eighteenth century. Apart from these three Romans, Poussin had one other close friend and patron, the Frenchman, Fréart de Chantelou, but it is characteristic of the manner in which the Royal collection was built up that, whereas a great part of the drawings by Poussin belonging to his Roman friends has come to Windsor, there is not one which can be traced to Chantelou's collection.

The Royal Library provides the best means available for the study of the early period of Poussin. It possesses the only works certainly produced by the artist before he settled in Rome in 1624, namely the illustrations to Ovid made for Marino in 1620–23, and also a very large proportion of the drawings dating from 1624–30. On the basis of this series we can form a quite clear idea of what the artist aimed at in his first years. Considered from the purely æsthetic point of view these drawings do not rank high in Poussin's œuvre. The line is coarse, schematic, and sometimes inexpressive, but it is vigorous, and the wash, in varying tones of bistre and grey, has something of the luminous quality which the artist attains in later works. From the historical point of view the Marino drawings are interesting in that they show Poussin in his pre-Roman days as a typical member of the Second School of Fontainebleau. This school, from which there is a single drawing in the Royal Library (No. 20), was one of the more classical manifestations of Late Mannerism, less extreme in its emotionalism and exaggeration than the contemporary schools in Flanders or Lorraine, but nevertheless Mannerist in its elongated and posturing figures, its abrupt foreshortenings and arbitrary use of perspective, and its schematic drawing of the human figure. To see how fully Poussin accepted these principles the reader need only look at the 'Polyphemis, Acis and Galatea' (No. 159) with the disparity of size between foreground and background figures, or the 'Orpheus in Hades' (No. 157) which is conspicuous among all Poussin's works for the borrowing of poses and types from Michelangelo's later works. These alone would be enough to prove that Poussin was either forgetting or concealing the truth when in later years he said that the only models of his youth had been ancient sculpture, Raphael and Giulio Romano. This inaccuracy is, however, comprehensible, for no classical artist living in the middle of the seventeenth century would have willingly admitted that he had once subscribed to the tenets of Mannerism, a creed which had been finally condemned by both artists and critics.

The Marino drawings are not without a certain beauty. They are not meant to be great works of art, nor are they preparations for serious paintings. They are intended to be complete in themselves —though it is quite likely that Poussin envisaged that they might be engraved for a new edition of Ovid—and the artist's aim is to tell the stories of the Metamorphoses in a light and tasteful way, with some of that allusiveness which Marino studied in his verse. For this reason the drawings are often difficult to interpret, since they seem to contain episodes to which Ovid makes no reference. It is possible that these additions are embroideries suggested by Marino himself.

The drawings dating from Poussin's first years in Rome are in many ways similar to the Marino series. The coarse line survives, but the affectation of the artist's early Mannerism gradually disappears. The subjects are usually Bacchic, and in some of them, such as No. 174, we see foreshadowed the great Bacchanal paintings of the middle 'thirties. The elements of the later design are there; but the character is wholly different. Poussin has put off Mannerism but he has not yet begun to move towards his later classicism. Instead he introduces an almost grotesque quality, particularly in his figure types. His satyrs are the most earthy of silvan creatures, vigorous and lecherous. 'Amor vincit omnia', the theme underlying one of the drawings of this time (No. 176), could almost be made the motto for the whole series. Never was Poussin so full-blooded as in these drawings and in certain paintings of the same time, in which for a moment he exploits the naturalism of the Caravaggiesques. Something of this naturalism also appears in the drawing of 'Le Fanciulle Rusticane' (No. 179), which is unique in Poussin's work in that it depicts a genre scene.

Before the end of the decade a new mood appears, particularly in certain religious and romantic subjects. For the first time Poussin turns to Tasso's epic, the *Gerusalemme Liberata*, for themes, and although at this stage he draws his inspiration from the great battle scenes (*cf.* No. 181) rather than from the love passages of the poem, this first contact with Tasso is significant of an impending change. In religious subjects a more serious tone appears, and Poussin uses to express it the formulae of Domenichino, the vital new influence at this stage. A drawing like No. 182, a study for the 'Triumph of David' at Dulwich, is executed almost in the manner of Domenichino's pen-sketches, and a very curious red chalk drawing of the Apostles from an Ascension (No. 183) shows how much Poussin learnt from the master's studies in this medium. On the other hand even at this stage

Poussin tends to be less meticulous than Domenichino, and we can see the first traces of that classical generalizing which is typical of his later manner.

In the early 'thirties Poussin's style as a draughtsman reaches its greatest charm, though not its greatest expressive power. His hand becomes more sure, and the line takes on a fluency which it had hitherto lacked. The designs are laid out with decision and spontaneity, and there is no fumbling, even when he is feeling his way towards a fully elaborated composition for a painting. This is particularly evident in the 'Saving of Pyrrhus' (No. 189) for which there are two sketches on the recto and verso of a single sheet showing different phases in the evolution of the design, each of which, however, is executed without hesitation or alteration.

Almost all the drawings of this period are executed in pen with bistre wash, and in the use of wash Poussin has made as great an advance as he has in the use of pure pen line. The wash is laid on in broad masses, not in small brush strokes, and its chief beauty lies in the astonishing variety of tone which it takes on in Poussin's hands. It can be delicate and limpid as in the 'Virginia' (No. 193), luminous as in the 'Agony' (No. 196) or dark and dramatic as in the 'Schoolmaster of Falerii' (No. 190). In a few cases Poussin uses the whole range of tones in a single drawing, as in the 'Pyrrhus' (No. 189), in which it can almost be said that he paints in wash.

The influence of the circle of Cassiano del Pozzo shows itself in Poussin's work of the later 'thirties in an increasing classicism of form. This is apparent in such a drawing as the lovely 'Confirmation' (No. 205) which is a preparation for a painting commissioned for Cassiano himself. The design is clearer and more logically planned than in earlier works, and tends more towards the type of composition found in ancient bas-reliefs. The figures are calmer and more static, and in the finished painting they assume poses which recall classical sculpture, though this tendency is never so visible in the preliminary sketches.

It was not, however, till Poussin's journey to Paris in 1641–42 that the new classicism reached its full expression; but in the 'Holy Family' (No. 213) executed during this visit it appears in its purest form. Poussin has gone beyond the academic classicism of Domenichino, which was itself an evolution from the tradition of the Carracci, and has revived his style by direct contact with antiquity. The Virgin stands here like a Roman Victory, with one foot raised on a block of stone in a typical classical pose.

After his contact in Paris with French intellectuals, another element comes into Poussin's work, which can be described as a tone of almost Stoical seriousness, combined with a Cartesian rationalism and a deep interest in psychological problems. The drawings of this period in the Royal Collection are not many, but there are enough to illustrate these new tendencies. The rough sketch of 'Medea murdering her children' (No. 217) and the more elaborate drawing of the 'Sacrifice of Polyxena' (No. 220) are typical both of Poussin's preference at this time for serious classical subjects as opposed to the Bacchic themes of his earlier years, and also of his desire to squeeze the full psychological and dramatic content out of a story. The 'Moses striking the Rock' (No. 218) shows his new and more serious attitude towards religious painting, for this is a subject which in his earlier days he would have treated as a sort of pageant, not as the miraculous and rather grim event which it becomes here.

Stylistically there is an equally great change in these later drawings. In the paintings of his later years Poussin deliberately gives up the charms of rich Venetian colour and attractive composition in favour of a more austere manner of design and colour; and an equivalent change can be seen in the drawings. The fluent line and rich wash of the 'thirties would have been a distraction from the seriousness of his purpose, and they are replaced by a line which seeks to note the exact psychological meaning of each gesture, irrespective of outward elegance, and wash which is used to model and to indicate dramatic effect rather than to create a surface immediately attractive to the eye.

One drawing recently discovered at Windsor among the Italian collection, 'The Three Marys at the Sepulchre' (No. 221), illustrates Poussin's style in his very last phase, when as an old man he was pursuing his researches into the means of expressing a story in its most concentrated form according to the classical canons which he had taken as his guide. Like a late drawing by Rembrandt this sketch seems at first sight to be a mere scribble, and its expressive simplicity reaches an abstract quality which almost defies analysis.

In addition to these originals by Poussin there are many among the drawings executed by his pupils which are of great interest for the light which they throw on his methods. In his earlier period he relied very little on assistants, but the decorative commissions which he received during his visit to Paris compelled him to use them, and on his return to Rome in 1642 he seems to have continued the practice to a certain extent. There are several instances in the Royal Library in which original sketches by Poussin exist side by side with finished versions made from them by pupils. The most interesting is the composition of 'Scipio and the Pirates' for which two originals are to be seen (No. 211 recto and verso), and also a very fine studio version (No. 251)—so fine, indeed, that one is tempted to wonder whether Poussin did not execute certain parts of it himself—which was probably made for Cardinal Francesco Barberini and sent to him from Paris. Another set illustrates Poussin's method in preparing the decorations for the Long Gallery of the Louvre, with which he was commissioned during his visit to Paris. A small original sketch (No. 214) shows how Poussin himself planned the panels, and a series of highly finished drawings (Nos. 252–6) represent the stage to which these designs were carried by his assistants before the full-scale execution.

There is no other French artist who can be studied at Windsor like Poussin in every phase and every mood; but the drawings by Claude form an impressive group, for their variety and for their extremely high quality. There are twenty-two drawings in the Royal Library certainly by this master, and nine more closely connected with him. Twelve of them are original drawings from nature, which formed part of a small note-book (Nos. 50–61), and which show the artist at his freshest and most spontaneous. They are the immediate records of his feelings in front of the landscape and buildings in Rome and the Campagna, and they combine the feeling for the ruins of antiquity with the subtlety of observation in light effects which constitute Claude's most obvious charm. The other drawings are fully worked out landscape compositions which, beside the sketches, seem at first sight, like Claude's paintings, artificial. But if Claude has here sacrificed freshness, he has amply made up for this loss by the romantic, other-worldly atmosphere which he infuses into them. Nor would it be fair to pass them over as mere dream creations, for they are distilled from precise observation of certain aspects of nature—observation for which there is no parallel at that time, nor indeed for several centuries to come.

Two drawings are of particular interest for the light which they throw on Claude's methods, namely the 'Apulian Shepherd' (No. 43) and the 'Acis and Galatea' (No. 42). In both of these Claude has employed a very unusual device. After completing the drawing on the recto of the sheet, he has turned the paper over and traced through a part of the design on the verso, and then developed it into a different composition from the recto. This trick seems to have been part of his elaborate method for developing his finished landscape compositions, and reminds one of the conscious way in which Poussin played about with the elements in his figure compositions, reversing them and rearranging them till they attained the exact harmony demanded by his scrupulous sensibility. This is but one example of the strict classicism of Claude's approach.

*   *   *   *   *

The scope and method of the present catalogue should perhaps be defined. It includes all the drawings in the Royal Library which could definitely be identified as French, including a few architectural designs, with the following exceptions:

1. The works of certain artists who, though French by birth, spent almost the whole of their career in England and will be included in the English school.

2. Certain drawings by French artists in the volumes of Military Costumes, of which it is intended ultimately to produce a separate catalogue. These drawings, though not given detailed entries in the present volume, are referred to under the name of the artists concerned.

In the catalogue itself the artists are divided into centuries and arranged alphabetically in each century. The plates, however, which are intended to show the evolution of French drawing, are arranged as far as possible in strict chronology. A clear distinction has been made in the catalogue between drawings classified as being definitely by a particular artist and those which are merely attributed to him. The more certain form is used only where the drawing can be connected with a painting or engraving, or where there is an old attribution supported by stylistic analysis. In one or two cases it has been used when style alone leaves no shadow of doubt about the authenticity of the work. In all other cases, especially with drawings which have been discovered among the mass of unsorted material in the Library, the more cautious form 'attributed to' has been preferred.

The debts which I have incurred in the preparation of this catalogue are many, partly owing to the nature of the task, and partly because of the difficult circumstances in which it has been carried out. To His Majesty The King I owe the privilege of working in the Royal Library at Windsor, a privilege of a peculiar value during the years of the War, when all other great collections of drawings were inaccessible for one reason or another. To the Royal Librarian, Sir Owen Morshead, I am indebted in both a general and a particular way: in general, because without his enthusiasm and energy this volume and the series of which it forms a part would never have been prepared; and in particular for the unfailing help which he and his assistants have given me in the many and tiresome practical problems which arise in preparing a catalogue of this kind. Mr. Paul Oppé has earned my deepest gratitude by undertaking the difficult and unrewarding task of preparing the catalogue entries for the nineteenth-century drawings, which for reasons of space have had to be reduced to the minimum. Dr. K. T. Parker has given me the benefit of his great knowledge of eighteenth-century French art by advising me over many of the problems arising out of the drawings of that period. Dr. Rudolf Wittkower and other members of the Warburg Institute have given me the clues to several difficult problems of iconography. Mr. Basil Gray and Miss Annemarie Meyer have also supplied me with valuable information about individual drawings. Miss Margaret Whinney has given me constant help by copying the whole manuscript and by checking and correcting a multitude of details. All the photographs of the drawings have been specially made by Mr. Alfred Carlebach.

To Dr. Walter Friedlaender my debt is great and difficult to define. As one of the pioneers in the study of Poussin his work will always be of the greatest value to all students of French art; but I have derived more from it than that. In collaborating with him and Dr. Rudolf Wittkower in preparing the first volume of the *Catalogue Raisonné* of Poussin's drawings I learnt much about the methods of that artist, and since the appearance of that volume I have had the advantage of using the material which he has collected for the remaining sections of the catalogue. This means that I have constantly had the advantage of referring to the best available corpus of photographs of Poussin's drawings, and I have therefore been able in the present catalogue to refer to drawings in other collections similar to those at Windsor. Moreover it was my privilege to collaborate in preparing for publication the part of the projected second volume dealing with historical subjects. This work was finished more than two years ago, but circumstances have so far prevented its publication. I have, however, included in the present catalogue certain identifications of historical subjects which I made for the *Catalogue Raisonné*. The entries for the mythological subjects have been made independently of Dr. Friedlaender's notes, but I find that in certain cases we have arrived at similar conclusions.

A.F.B.

CATALOGUE

BIBLIOGRAPHY

The following abbreviations are used for the works most frequently referred to in the catalogue:

Andresen. A. Andresen. Nicolaus Poussin. Verzeichniss der nach seinen Gemälden gefertigten Kupferstiche. Leipzig, 1863.

Chamberlaine. J. Chamberlaine. Original Designs of the most celebrated Masters . . . in His Majesty's Collection. London, 1812.

Dussieux. L. Dussieux. Les artistes français à l'étranger. Third edition, 1876.

F.A.Q.R. Fine Arts Quarterly Review.

Friedlaender, Drawings. Walter Friedlaender. The Drawings of Nicolas Poussin. Catalogue Raisonné. Volume 1, edited in collaboration with R. Wittkower and A. Blunt. London, 1939.

Grautoff. N. Grautoff. Nicolas Poussin. Munich, 1914.

Grosvenor Gallery Publications. The Royal Collection of Drawings by the Old Masters at Windsor. Reproduced by S. Thompson. London, n.d.

Hind. British Museum. Catalogue of the Drawings of Claude Lorrain. London, 1926.

L.V. Richard Earlom. Liber Veritatis. A Collection of Prints after the original Designs of Claude Le Lorrain. London, 1777–1819.

Lemoisne. 1912. P. A. Lemoisne. Eugène Lami. Paris, 1912.

Lemoisne. 1914. P. A. Lemoisne. L'Œuvre d'Eugène Lami. Société de l'Histoire de l'Art français. Paris, 1914.

Mémoires Inédits. P. Dussieux. Mémoires Inédits sur la Vie et les Ouvrages des Membres de l'Académie de Peinture et de Sculpture. Paris, 1854.

Poussin, Correspondance. C. Jouanny. Correspondance de Nicolas Poussin. Société de l'Histoire de l'Art français. Paris, 1911.

R. Davies. Randall Davies. Victorian Water-colours at Windsor Castle. London, 1937.

THE DRAWINGS

FIFTEENTH CENTURY

JEAN FOUQUET (c. 1420–c. 1480). (After.)

1. Portrait of a papal legate to the French Court.
No. 13051.

196 mm. × 144 mm. Red chalk.

Literature: *French Art*, R.A., 1932, p. 121.

An exact copy of the drawing formerly in the Oppenheimer Collection (cf. *French Art*, R.A., 1932, p. 121, No. 541) without the inscription on the original. The copy appears to have been made in the sixteenth century.

SIXTEENTH CENTURY

JACQUES ANDROUET DU CERCEAU THE ELDER (c. 1510–after 1584).

In one of the volumes of architectural drawings (A12) are three sketches attributed to this artist (Nos. 10439, 10495, 10496). Since, however, two of them represent parts of the architecture of the Vatican and the third plans and details from ancient Roman buildings, they will be dealt with in the catalogues of Italian architectural drawings and of drawings after the antique respectively. The most important of the three (No. 10496) has been published by Ashby (*Papers of the British School at Rome*, vi, 1913, p. 197 ff.) and by Dagobert Frey (*Michelangelo-Studien*, 1920, p. 20 ff.). All three bear inscriptions in French in a hand which Ashby believed to be that of the elder du Cerceau.

FRANÇOIS CLOUET (Before 1522–1572). (After.)

2. Portrait of a lady in mourning.   No. 13068.

319 mm. × 189 mm. Red and black chalk.

Copy of a drawing in the Salting Collection in the British Museum which bears an inscription: *Madame de Savoie*. This could only refer to Marguerite, fourth daughter of Francis I, who married Philibert Emmanuel, duc de Savoie. On the other hand, the Windsor drawing is entirely unlike other portraits of the lady, and the sitter is here represented in widow's dress, whereas Marguerite pre-deceased her husband. The identification must therefore be regarded as improbable in spite of the inscription.

The drawing may be by the same hand which made those in the volume now at Knowsley (cf. Moreau-Nélaton, *Les Clouet et leurs Emules*, 1924, ii, Figs. 387, etc.).

3. Scene from a French farce.   *Pl. 1.* No. 6445.

168 mm. × 177 mm. Black chalk.

Literature: A. E. Popham, 'A drawing by François Clouet?' *Die graphischen Künste*, N.F., iv, 1939, p. 3.

This drawing was identified by A. E. Popham as being a preparation for an engraving published by Nicolas Le Blon after Clouet, dated 1579. (The engraving is published by J. Adhémar, 'Deux Scènes de Comédie gravées d'après François Clouet', *Die graphischen Künste*, N.F., ii, 1937, p. 137.) Popham considers whether the drawing can be by Clouet himself, but concludes that it is by the engraver after a lost original. The identity in size between drawing and engraving suggests that it is a direct preparation for the latter, but there is one further significant detail. In the drawing the arms of the scribe and the woman overlap, but both are drawn in completely so that their outlines intersect. No original artist would do this in so finished a work. This curious detail suggests, moreover, that the draughtsman was not exactly copying an original, but was putting together elements which were not originally intended to stand in this relation. Now Adhémar (*loc. cit.*, p. 138) publishes another version of this subject, a wood-engraving by the younger Jean de Gourmont (Fig. 1), in which the figures in the drawing occur, together with others, in a more elaborate composition. The scribe and the doctor stand on the left, in the opposite sense to the drawing. In the middle stand two women arguing, one of whom is almost identical with the figure in the drawing, this time in the same sense. On the right is a fantastic group of carnival carousers. Adhémar concludes that Jean de Gourmont knew the Clouet composition shown in the Le Blon engraving and has adapted it. But it seems more likely that his engraving is a copy of a lost composition by Clouet, and that the author of the Windsor drawing selected certain figures from this lost original, altering their relative positions and reversing a part of the group, to make a new smaller composition. This view is slightly confirmed by the fact that the action of the woman is far more logical in the Gourmont composition, in which she is arguing with her opposite number, than in the drawing, in which her relation to the other group is not very clear.

Popham states that the impression of the Le Blon engraving is dated 1579, and Adhémar gives 1590–96 as the date for the Gourmont version, but without stating any reasons. On the face of it, Adhémar's suggestion is unlikely, since the Clouet composition would have seemed archaic in the last decade of the sixteenth century. Moreover, the italic type of the verses below the engraving indicates a much earlier period. We do not know exactly when Gourmont began work in Paris, but he was certainly active there by 1575, and already lived at the address given on the woodcut. It is quite probable that his engraving is earlier than Le Blon's, and not later, as Adhémar supposes. It is even possible that it may have been made before Clouet's death in 1572. The most probable solution to the whole problem

Fig. 1. JEAN DE GOURMONT: French Farce. *Woodcut*

seems, therefore, to be that there was an original drawing by Clouet, now lost, which is more or less accurately rendered by Gourmont, and that in or just before 1579 an unknown draughtsman made the Windsor drawing as a variation of Clouet's original. The Windsor drawing was then engraved (with small differences in the background figures) for Le Blon.

The subject of the drawing cannot be easily identified, but the inscription on the engraving shows that the artist's intention is to defend farce as a genre. It reads:

> La farce des Grecx Decendue
> Hommes sur tous Ingenieux
> C'est par nostre france rendue
> Pour remonstrer Jeusnes et vieulx.
> Elle taxe les vicieulx
> les Dévoiex elle radresse
> et rend petits les glorieulx
> chantant Du monde la finesse.

ETIENNE DELAUNE (1519–1584). (Attributed to.)

4. Design for a cup.   *Pl. 2.* No. 13052.

188 mm. × 101 mm. Irregularly cut. Pen and bistre wash on vellum.

On the top of the cup is a figure of Neptune. The stem is formed of three mermaids and the base of dolphins. The whole is elaborately decorated with arabesques.

Probably a design for a metal cup, but possibly for a piece of St. Porchaire pottery. The attribution to Delaune is based on the similarity to drawings in the Louvre (Nos. 3544–3547) in the same style and technique, and also on vellum.

5. Design for a ewer.   *Pl. 3.* No. 13053.

247 mm. × 105 mm. Cut round the outline of the drawing. Pen and grey-mauve wash on vellum.

Decorated with mythological scenes and ornamental devices. The central medallion represents Apollo and Daphne, and the handle is formed of a figure of Daphne being transformed into a laurel. The subjects of the other two panels cannot be identified exactly, but that on the left represents the pursuit of a nymph, and that on the right appears to depict Diana resting after the hunt. On the neck are tritons and under the lip a winged and bearded figure who may be a wind-god. The foot is composed of dolphins.

Probably a design for a gold or enamelled ewer.

LAGNEAU (active end of sixteenth and beginning of seventeenth century). (Attributed to.)

6. Portrait of Nicolas de Neufville, Seigneur de Villeroy.
                                                   No. 13069.

220 mm. × 180 mm. The head itself on a separate piece of paper 114 mm. × 77 mm.; the frame added. Head in red chalk and grey wash. The frame in grey wash. Inscribed on the frame: *Portrait de Nicolas de Neufville et Seigneur de Villeroi et d'Alincour Gouverneur de Lyon.*

Nicolas de Neufville (1543–1617), who became Marquis de Villeroy in 1615, was an important administrator under the last Valois kings, under Henry IV and during the minority of Louis XIII, for which period his *Mémoires* are important documents. A portrait of him in youth by François Quesnel is to be found in the Bibliothèque Nationale (cf. Dimier, *Histoire de la Peinture de Portrait en France au XVIᵉ Siècle*, 1924, i, pl. 53). Thomas de Leu and Michel Lasne also engraved portraits of him.

This portrait is executed with the detailed naturalism connected with Lagneau, but the scale is smaller and the execution more delicate than his usual work, and the attribution must be regarded as tentative.

The ornamental frame, a later addition, probably dating from the second half of the seventeenth century, includes the arms of the family with a marquis' coronet. The inscription contains an inaccuracy, for Nicolas de Neufville was never governor of Lyon. It was his eldest son Charles, the father of the Marshal de Villeroy, who held this post. The Windsor drawing may be connected with the engraved portrait by Thomas de Leu, which is not at present accessible.

FRANCESCO PRIMATICCIO (1504–1570). (After.)

7. Mars, Venus, Cupid and Apollo. No. 13055.

230 mm. × 314 mm. Black chalk. Inscribed: *a Fontanebelleau.*

In his description of the palace of Fontainebleau, written in 1625, Cassiano del Pozzo described a room occupied by the Princesse de Conti: 'dipinta a quadretti ripartati con festoni e statue di stucco affresco con istorie favolose, fra le quale la principale era degl'Amori di Marte e Venere scoperti dal Sole' (cf. E. Müntz and E. Molinier, 'Le Château de Fontainebleau au 17ᵉ siècle d'après des documents inédits', *Mémoires de la Société de l'Histoire de Paris*, 1886, p. 255). This fresco is now lost, but the present drawing is presumably a copy after it, including indications of the surrounding stucco decorations. Dimier (*Le Primatice*, 1900, p. 451, No. 145) mentions a drawing of this subject by Primaticcio in the Albertina. It has not, however, been possible to compare it with the Windsor drawing. The style of the drawing suggests a French artist of the early seventeenth century, and the spelling *Fontanebelleau* in the inscription points to an Italian connection. These facts, taken in conjunction with the close connection of Cassiano del Pozzo with many drawings at Windsor, suggest that the copy may perhaps have been made for him at the time of his visit in 1625.

8. Diana and Neptune. No. 13056.

219 mm. × 274 mm. Black chalk. Inscribed: *a Fontanebelleau.*

A copy after the fresco by Primaticcio on the right of the mantelpiece in the Salle de Bal at Fontainebleau, engraved by Beton. Dimier (*Le Primatice*, 1900, p. 451,

No. 146) mentions a drawing for this composition in the Albertina. The Windsor drawing is by the same hand as No. 7, and has an identical inscription. It may, therefore, also possibly have belonged to Cassiano del Pozzo.

The original drawings by Primaticcio will be dealt with in the catalogue of Italian drawings.

FRANÇOIS QUESNEL (1543–1619). (Attributed to.)

9. Portrait of a young man. *Pl. 4.* No. 13066.

305 mm. × 227 mm. Black and red chalk and water-colour.

10. Portrait of a woman. No. 13065.

308 mm. × 231 mm. Black and red chalk and water-colour.

11. Portrait of a woman in a widow's or nun's cap. No. 13061.

307 mm. × 225 mm. Black and red chalk and water-colour.

12. Portrait of a woman. No. 13059.

308 mm. × 229 mm. Black and red chalk and water-colour.

13. Portrait of a woman. *Pl. 5.* No. 13057.

305 mm. × 228 mm. Black and red chalk and water-colour.

14. Portrait of a woman. No. 13067.

322 mm. × 234 mm. Black and red chalk and water-colour.

15. Portrait of a woman. No. 13062.

315 mm. × 238 mm. Black chalk and water-colour.

16. Portrait of a woman. No. 13063.

345 mm. × 254 mm. Black and red chalk and water-colour.

17. Portrait of a woman. No. 13064.

325 mm. × 235 mm. Black chalk and water-colour.

18. Portrait of a woman. No. 13060.

346 mm. × 255 mm. Black and red chalk and water-colour.

19. Portrait of a bearded man. No. 13058.

302 mm. × 224 mm. Black and red chalk and water-colour.

The drawings are traditionally attributed to 'Dumonstier', but they bear no resemblance to the style of any member of that family. It is impossible without a careful comparison with other sixteenth-century chalk portraits in the original to arrive at any definite conclusion about their authorship. They are, however, very close indeed to a group of portraits of which the greater part are in the Bibliothèque Nationale and which are attributed by Dimier confidently (*Histoire de la Peinture de Portrait en France au 16ᵉ Siècle*, 1924, p. 158 ff.) and by Moreau-Nélaton more hesitantly (*Les Clouet et leurs Emules*, 1924, ii, p. 37 ff.) to François Quesnel. Most of the portraits of women (i.e. Nos. 12–18) are similar in general character to the drawing of Henriette d'Entragues (Moreau-Nélaton, *op. cit.*, i, Fig. 82) on which the attribution to Quesnel is based by Dimier. Moreover, No. 13 is identical in pose and dress, even to such details as the necklace, with the portrait of the Comtesse de Brissac (Moreau-Nélaton, *op. cit.*, ii, Fig. 232).

Certain of the Windsor drawings seem at first sight to stand slightly apart from the group just discussed. But they are in fact probably by the same hand. They are all in exactly the same technique, which includes the use of water-colour for eyes, hair and usually face—a rarity in portraits of this type. The two portraits of women not included in the group discussed above are exactly similar in handling to No. 12, although they differ in the layout on the page. The two portraits of men are more strikingly different, but both can be closely paralleled in other drawings of the group attributed to Quesnel. No. 9 is in general very near to the Henri de Gondi (Moreau-Nélaton, *op. cit.*, ii, Fig. 240), and, in the handling of hair and dress, to the Vidame de Chartres and the Marquis de Ragny (*ibid.*, ii, Figs. 230, 228). No. 19, with its fine and rather scratchy lines in hair and beard, recalls the Sieur de Fourcy (*ibid.*, ii, Fig. 238) and more remotely the Baron de Contenant and the Sieur de Clusseos (*ibid.*, ii, Figs. 236, 237).

The differences in style between these various drawings can probably be accounted for to some extent by the differences in their dates, which can be established by their dress. Nos. 9 and 10 are the earliest, c. 1575–85. Nos. 12–18 are a little later, 1585–95, and No. 19 is 1590–1600. No. 11 is harder to date, since the dress of widows and nuns changed more slowly. Stylistically, however, the drawing is to be associated with No. 10, and therefore probably dates from 1575–85.

As is usually the case with drawings of this type when they do not bear inscriptions, there is no clue to the identity of the sitters.

It is possible that these drawings represent the surviving fragment of the volume which was in the possession of Charles I, and which is listed by Vanderdoort as containing forty-nine portraits 'in dry colours of the chiefest Nobility and famous men at that time in France' (*A Catalogue and Description of King Charles the First's Capital Collection*, 1757, item 42). Vanderdoort states that the volume was presented to the King by the Duc de Liancourt.

ANONYMOUS ARTIST, SECOND SCHOOL OF FONTAINEBLEAU, c. 1590–1600.

20. Rinaldo leaving Armida.   *Pl. 6.* No. 0153.

224 mm. × 373 mm. Pen and bistre wash.

The subject is taken from Tasso (*Gerusalemme Liberata*, xvi, 59 ff.), who describes how Rinaldo was dragged away from Armida by the two knights Carlo and Ubaldo.

The drawing belongs to the Second School of Fontainebleau and is related to the style of Ambroise Dubois and Toussaint Dubreuil, though it cannot be definitely attributed to either. It is possible, however, that it may be connected with a cycle of paintings illustrating Tasso executed by the former in conjunction with Testelin in the Queen's apartment in the Louvre. The only other known Tasso series of this period, painted for the Queen at Fontainebleau, also by Dubois, dealt with the story of Clorinda.

SEVENTEENTH CENTURY

CLAUDE BERTIN (? –1705).

21. Apollo attended by the nymphs of Thetis. No. 6178.

299 mm. × 413 mm. Pen and grey wash. Inscribed in an early eighteenth-century hand: *Bertin*.

Described in the eighteenth-century manuscript catalogue as: 'Apollo attended by the Muses'.

The drawing shows the group of sculpture executed by Girardon and Regnaudin for the Grotte de Thétis at Versailles about 1666–1672. The grotto was destroyed in 1686 and the group was removed to the Bains d'Apollon where it remained till the year 1705. After modifications in this year, and again in 1725, it was finally worked into Hubert Robert's remodelling of the fountains in 1775. The present drawing shows the group on the original base on which it stood in the grotto, together with the additions made at the sides when it was moved to the Bains d'Apollon in 1686 (cf. painting by Cotelle in Nolhac, *Les Jardins de Versailles*, 1906, p. 119, and the engraving after this painting by Simonneau dated 1688). In 1705 the base was again altered, so that the drawing must have been made between 1686 and 1705. This shows that the Bertin referred to in the inscription must be Claude Bertin who worked at Versailles from 1685 onwards. It is known, moreover, that he was engaged on the alterations and restorations of the sculpture in the gardens, and it is quite likely that this drawing is a design for the new disposition of the group when it was moved in 1686.

JACQUES CALLOT (1592–1635).

22. The Palazzo Pitti.   *Pl. 7.* No. 4614.

226 mm. × 328 mm. Pen and bistre on vellum. Signed: *I. Callot fecit 1630.*

Described in the manuscript catalogue, among drawings by Stefano della Bella, as: 'The front and ascent to the Pallazzo Pitti, as once designed but never compleated'.

This drawing is of capital importance for the history of the various projects for the completion of the Pitti. In 1630, when the drawing was made, the Pitti consisted of a block of three storeys, of thirteen bays each, seven dating from the original construction of the fifteenth century, and six added in 1620 by Giulio Parigi for Cosimo II. In 1640, however, Alfonso Parigi, the son of Giulio, continued his father's work and extended the two lower storeys to their present extent of twenty-five bays, and his addition follows exactly the lines indicated in Callot's drawing of 1630. Moreover, when the two wings were added at the end of the eighteenth and the beginning of the nineteenth century, they also followed in general disposition, though not in detail, the scheme shown by Callot. The steps shown in the drawing were never executed.

It is therefore evident that Callot is not merely inventing for his own amusement a fantastic expansion of the palace, but that he must have known plans actually in existence for a real extension. Baldinucci, in his life of Cigoli, writes as follows: 'By order of the same Grand Duke Ferdinand he made a fine design for the enlargement and completion of the Palazzo Pitti. In this he expressed a plan of his own, which was to avoid damaging what had been built before his time, to level the square (which slopes sharply down towards the road) as much as was necessary for the convenient passage and turning of coaches, which were to be driven up from the other part of the square by a double way which broke the rise from this level. The part in front of the door he made much broader and in the form of an ellipse. And below the steps two beautiful fountains were to be placed. He next threw out at the sides two wings, the whole width of the square extending right over to the road. These had the same Tuscan order and the same windows with grilles on the ground floor. And below these wings, which joined on to the ground floor of the palace, he introduced vaulted passages, suitable for the use of the court servants, and horsemen, or for the coaches themselves. The two wings rose up to the level of the second row of windows, where they ended in a fine loggia.'

Now Callot's drawing follows this scheme in almost every detail: the slope, the steps, the two fountains, the wings with arcades, terraces and Tuscan order. The only differences are that Callot shows the façade extended to 25 bays with a fourth storey of seven bays, which is not mentioned by Cigoli, and he crowns his building with statues. It is interesting to note that Pietro da Cortona in his schemes for modernizing the Palazzo Pitti (c. 1640) also planned a fourth storey.

Venturi, who quotes the above description (*Storia dell' Arte Italiana*, XI, ii, p. 487), associates it with a series of sketches by Buontalenti in the Uffizi. In certain respects the Callot drawing fits the written account more accurately (cf. the two fountains, the Tuscan order, the arcades below the wings). In two points it seems at first sight less close. For the description does not mention the extension of the façade in width, nor the addition of the fourth floor. On the other hand it is hard to see how the arcades under the wings could have been worked in unless the façade was sufficiently broadened to make the wings stand free from the carriage slopes (in the Buotalenti drawings they flank these slopes). A fourth floor of seven bays is, moreover, indicated in two of the Buontalenti sketches, though here it takes the form of an open loggia.

It is very probable, as Venturi suggests, that Baldinucci has made a mistake and has attributed to Cigoli a plan which was really Buontalenti's, for the drawings in the Uffizi are certainly his. This supposition is confirmed by the details of the design preserved by Callot in which the steps are typical of Buontalenti's style, and unlike any work of Cigoli.

Callot's drawing seems to represent a final stage of the plans for completing the Pitti, of which the various Buontalenti sketches indicate the preliminary developments. It might be thought that it embodies the ideas of one of the Parigi, produced as an extension of the Buontalenti scheme. But the two facts that it agrees with the description given by Baldinucci of Ferdinand I's project and that the steps are exactly in Buontalenti's manner and connected with one of the Uffizi drawings (Venturi, *op. cit.*, pl. 439) provide a strong indication that it is based on plans of the earlier date. If this is so, it proves that the additions of Giulio and Alfonso Parigi in 1620 and 1640 were part of Ferdinand I's conception, and that even the wings, added a century and a half later, were executed in the spirit of this scheme.

23. La Rue Neuve de Nancy.   *Pl. 8.* No. 4615.

142 mm. × 495 mm. Pen and bistre. Much rubbed.

Described in the manuscript catalogue as: 'The fair or Carnival at Nancy in Lorrain'. A finished study for the engraving of 1628 known as 'La Rue Neuve de Nancy' (Meaume No. 621) in the same sense and on the same scale. It has been slightly cut on the left and at the top and bottom. Many of the groups in the foreground differ in their placing from the engraving. The drawing has suffered badly, but it appears to be of excellent quality and is certainly not a copy as has been suggested.

24. Study of a man.   *Pl. 12.* No. 4635.

251 mm. × 117 mm. Pen and bistre. Inscribed: *Calott.*

25. Study of a man.   *Pl. 13.* No. 4634.

258 mm. × 120 mm. Pen and bistre with traces of red chalk.

These two drawings come from a volume of sketches by Stefano della Bella at Windsor, and in spite of the inscription *Calott* on one of them they have up till now been attributed to the Italian artist. Even without the evidence supplied by the inscription the style of the drawings would be enough to justify an attribution to Callot himself. Stefano della Bella was always more delicate and less vigorous than this.

The drawings are not directly connected with any known engravings, but they are close in character to the *Noblesse Lorraine*, c. 1625, and also, though less exactly, to the *Fantaisies* of 1635. They probably, therefore, date from about 1625–35.

JACQUES CALLOT. (Attributed to.)

26. A man leaning on a parapet.   No. 4624.

84 mm. × 64 mm. Red chalk.

27. A man playing dice.   *Pl. 9.* No. 4625.

82 mm. × 64 mm. Red chalk.

28. Two seated men.   *Pl. 11.* No. 4627.

84 mm. × 113 mm. Red chalk.

29. Three men.   No. 4626.

84 mm. × 114 mm. Red and black chalk.

30. Two men.   *Pl. 10.* No. 4629.

85 mm. × 114 mm. Red and black chalk.

31. A priest and a musician.   No. 4628.

80 mm. × 108 mm. Red and black chalk, on two pieces of paper joined together.

These six drawings apparently form part of a single note-book. Like Nos. 24 and 25 they come from the volume containing drawings by Stefano della Bella. It is hard to distinguish original Callots from Stefano's skilful imitation of his manner, but in this case the connections with engravings by Callot are close enough to justify an attribution to him. The left-hand figure in No. 30 is extremely close to the twelfth engraving in the 'Capricci' (Meaume 795) and appears to be of the same model. The left-hand figures in No. 28 appear almost exactly in the 'Battaglia del Re Tessi e del Re Tinta' (Meaume 617), and both the figures in the drawing bear some likeness to the second of the 'Capricci' (Meaume 775). These connections suggest that the drawings were probably made in Florence about 1617–19.

Three other similar drawings, apparently from the same sketch-book, are in the collection of Sir Robert Witt.

GUILLAUME COURTOIS, *Il Borgognone* (1628–1679). (Attributed to.)

32. The Nativity.   No. 6803.

379 mm. × 268 mm. Black and red chalk, heightened with white, on greenish paper. Squared. Inscribed: *Borgognone*.

The attribution is based on the eighteenth-century inscription but is consistent with Courtois' more classical manner.

JACQUES COURTOIS, *Il Borgognone* (1621–1675).

33. A battle outside a town.   *Pl. 101.* No. 6344.

163 mm. × 256 mm. Pen and bistre wash.

34. A battle.   *Pl. 102.* No. 6343.

189 mm. × 262 mm. Pen and bistre wash.

These two drawings are typical of Courtois' style as illustrated in the well-authenticated drawings such as the sketch-book in the Louvre (No. 2737 ff.).

35. A battle.   No. 0868.

124 mm. × 273 mm. Pen and bistre with grey wash.

A less finished sketch than Nos. 33 and 34, but similar to them in draughtsmanship.

JACQUES COURTOIS, *Il Borgognone* (School of).

36. A camp scene.   No. 6340.

190 mm. × 292 mm. Pen and bistre wash.

A much damaged drawing, rather weak and lacking the movement usual in Courtois' drawing. Probably by an imitator.

GASPARD DUGHET, called GASPARD POUSSIN (1615–1675). (Attributed to.)

37. View of Tivoli.   No. 6134.

254 mm. × 412 mm. Pen and bistre, heightened with white, on blue paper.

38. Italian landscape.   No. 6133.

258 mm. × 406 mm. Pen and bistre, heightened with white, on blue paper.

A pair by the same hand. The general conception is near to Dughet, but the handling is somewhat Italian. The drawings are probably by Dughet when not working under the direct influence of Nicolas Poussin. In any case they are by the same hand as others traditionally attributed to him (cf. one belonging to Lady Lucas, *Vasari Society Reproductions*, Second Series, Part iii, No. 17).

GASPARD DUGHET, called GASPARD POUSSIN (School of).

39. Landscape with a road and a stream.   No. 6131.

259 mm. × 404 mm. Black chalk on brown paper heightened with white.

The general character of the landscape recalls Dughet's compositions, but the technique suggests that the drawing is probably by an Italian imitator.

40. Landscape with river.   No. 3541.

121 mm. × 343 mm. Black chalk.

This drawing, found among the Italian landscapes at Windsor, is clearly French in character. In detail it is near to the manner of Gaspard Dughet, and is probably by a French imitator.

CLAUDE GELLEE, *Le Lorrain* (1600–1682).

The drawings by Claude at Windsor include two principal groups: first a series of highly finished compositions, secondly a set of sketches from nature, mainly apparently from one note-book. Nothing is known of the provenance of these drawings, but the bulk of them, 'eight landscapes mostly large drawings' and 'seventeen small studies' are mentioned in the manuscript catalogue as being in a volume of *Paesi di Claudio Loranese e Altri*. This indicates that they came from an Italian collection, and certain facts suggest that they may, like the Poussin volume, have belonged to Cardinal Massimi. For the composition drawings mostly date from the last period of Claude's life when the Cardinal was one of his patrons, and one of them, 'The Temple of Apollo at Delphi' (No. 47) is for a painting commissioned by him. This is, however, only speculation, and they may well have been bought with the Albani collection.

A. Compositions.

41. The marriage of Isaac and Rebecca.
                            Pl. 72. No. 13076.

341 mm. × 444 mm. Black chalk, pen and bistre wash, heightened with white. Inscribed on verso: *Claudio Lorense vero. Claudio iv fecit.* (The second inscription is in Claude's handwriting.)

Literature: Chamberlaine, pl. 32; *Grosvenor Gallery Publications*; Pattison, *Claude Lorrain*, p. 279, No. 5; *Seventeenth Century Art*, R.A., 1938, p. 170, No. 498.

The subject is apparently the same as in two paintings, sometimes called 'the Mill', one painted for Prince Pamfili and now in the Doria Gallery, and the other executed in 1648 for the Duc de Bouillon, and now in the National Gallery (L.V. 113; cf. also Friedlaender, *Claude Lorrain*, pp. 64, 65).

Other similar scenes which may represent the same subject are as follows:

(1) A painting in the Louvre, dated 1639 (L.V.13; cf. Friedlaender, *Claude Lorrain*, p. 46). A replica, dated 1669, was, according to Mrs. Pattison (*Claude Lorrain*, p. 236), in the Yarborough collection.

(2) A painting in the Duke of Westminster's collection (cf. Friedlaender, *Claude Lorrain*, p. 87).

(3) Two etchings, R.D.6 and 10, c. 1636 and 1639 (cf. Friedlaender, *Claude Lorrain*, pp. 134, 135).

A drawing for the Westminster painting is L.V. III, 62, and another related to it is in the British Museum (Hind,

199). Mrs. Pattison mentions a drawing for the Pamfili or Bouillon versions in the Seymour-Haden collection.

42. *Recto:* Acis and Galatea.   *Pl. 73.* No. 13077.

353 mm. × 465 mm. Pen and bistre wash, heightened with white, on brown paper.

Literature: Chamberlaine, pl. 38; Pattison, *Claude Lorrain*, p. 279, No. 2.

Verso: The same subject.

Pen and bistre.

The subject is taken from Ovid, *Met.*, xiii, 870.

A study for the painting at Dresden dated 1657 and executed for M. Delagard (L.V.141). The drawing differs in many ways from the final version, but must date from about the same period.

On the verso the figures and part of the trees and drapery on the recto have been traced through by Claude himself, who has experimented with a different setting for the scene. He seems, however, to have given up the ideas he tried out here, for the painting is nearer to the recto version.

43. *Recto:* The Apulian shepherd changed into an olive tree.   *Pl. 77.* No. 13075.

351 mm. × 465 mm. Black chalk, pen and bistre wash with white, on brown paper. Some water-colour in the figures.

Literature: Chamberlaine, pl. 41; Pattison, *Claude Lorrain*, p. 279, No. 4.

Verso: The same subject.   *Pl. 76.*

Black chalk, pen and bistre.

The subject is from Ovid, *Met.*, xiv, 517.

A study for the painting executed for M. Delagard in 1657 and now at Bridgewater House (L.V.142), perhaps as a pendant to the 'Acis and Galatea'. A free preliminary sketch is in the Teyler Museum, Haarlem (cf. Hind, *The Drawings of Claude Lorrain*, pl. 1 b).

As in the last drawing the figures and some of the trees have been traced through on the verso, in this case in black chalk. These tracings are crude, but were probably made by Claude himself, since he certainly drew the new setting of trees in the middle and right background which are added in pen.

It is difficult to establish the order in which the two Windsor versions and the Teyler sketch were made. The Teyler drawing is in manner a freely drawn first sketch, but in its more open background it is closer to the painting than either of the Windsor versions. On the other hand the recto of the Windsor drawing shows the group of playing nymphs on the right, as in the painting, whereas in the verso Windsor sketch and in the Teyler sketch they are on the left. In all three drawings the shepherd is at one end of the composition, whereas in the painting he is moved to the middle. On the whole it looks as though Claude first made the Windsor recto drawing, then traced it through and experimented with the composition in reverse—since one must assume that the verso was drawn after the recto. The Teyler sketch would then represent a new attempt at a more open composition, based on the Windsor verso drawing, in which the idea of a central tree appears. A further approach to the painting can be seen in the introduction into the Teyler sketch of a third group, consisting of more nymphs with musical instruments, balancing those on the left. The new conception was later modified by a rearrangement of the figures, involving the transfer of the playing nymphs to the right, and the shepherd to the centre of the composition. It is characteristic of Claude's lack of invention in figure drawing that many of the figures appear unchanged in attitude throughout all these modifications of the composition.

44. St. John the Baptist preaching.   *Pl. 75.* No. 13082.
218 mm. × 257 mm. Pen and bistre, with bistre and grey wash, on buff paper.
Literature: Chamberlaine, pl. 59; Pattison, *Claude Lorrain*, p. 280, No. 6.
An elaborate drawing, not connected with any known painting. Another drawing of this subject is in the British Museum (Hind, 269).

45. *Recto:* Moses and the Burning Bush.
                    Pl. 78. No. 13083.
186 mm. × 292 mm. Pen, bistre wash and black chalk.
Literature: *Grosvenor Gallery Publications.*
A study for the painting in Bridgewater House, painted for M. de Bourlemont in 1664 (L.V.161). Other drawings for the same composition are in the British Museum (dated 1660, Hind, 250, engraved by Earlom, L.V. III, 45, when in the Spencer collection), and at Chatsworth (L.V. III, 99). The present drawing is very close to the British Museum version. Another drawing for a different version of the same subject is also at Chatsworth (L.V. III, 95). The chalk drawing of the trees in the background is close to a sketch in the Teyler Museum, Haarlem (cf. Hind, *The Drawings of Claude Lorrain*, pl. 69), dated 1671. The present drawing probably dates, like the British Museum version and the painting, from 1660–65.
Verso: Figure of a man, apparently fishing.
Pen and bistre.

46. The crossing of the Red Sea.   *Pl. 79.* No. 13080.
274 mm. × 367 mm. Pen with bistre and grey wash, heightened with white. Signed on verso: *Cladio ivf.*
Literature: Chamberlaine, pl. 48; Pattison, *Claude Lorrain*, p. 280, No. 7.
A finished drawing, with elaborately drawn figures, not connected with any known painting, or with any composition in the *Liber Veritatis.*
Probably a late drawing c. 1670–80.

47. The Temple of Apollo at Delphi.   *Pl. 74.* No. 13079.
254 mm. × 318 mm. Pen and bistre with grey wash.
Inscribed in Claude's handwriting: *Il tempio di Apollo in delfo sopra l monte parnaso(?) cavata da giustino historico* and on a rock in the foreground: *Claud(e) ivf Roma 1672 Ro(ma).*
Literature: Chamberlaine, pl. 50, Pattison, *Claude Lorrain*, p. 279, No. 3.
Elaborate study for L.V.182; the painting, now lost, was executed for Cardinal Massimi in 1673.

As indicated in the inscription, which is incorrectly given by Mrs. Pattison, the subject is taken from Justinus the historian, who describes the sanctuary of Delphi as follows in his *Historiae Philippicae* (xxiv, 6): 'The Temple of Apollo is situate on Mount Parnassus, on a rock steep on all sides.... Thus not walls but precipices, not defences formed by hand, but by nature protect the temple and the city..... The central part of the rock falls back in the shape of an amphitheatre..... In the winding of the rock about half way up the hill, there is a small plain, and in it a deep fissure in the ground, which is open for giving oracles.' Claude has followed closely the details supplied by Justinus, a source rarely drawn upon in painting, whom he probably read in the Italian translation of Tommaso Porcacchi, published in Venice in 1561.

The elements in the drawing recur in the version recorded in the *Liber Veritatis*, but rearranged. A similar procession with a sacrificial bull is to be found in the painting of 'The Temple of Apollo on the island of Delos' for Prince Pamfili (L.V.119), now in the Doria Gallery.

48. The landing of Æneas in Italy.   *Pl. 86.* No. 13081.
257 mm. × 335 mm. Pen and bistre, with bistre and grey wash. Signed: *Claudio ivf Roma 1677.*
Literature: Chamberlaine, pl. 35; *Grosvenor Gallery Publications*; Pattison, *Claude Lorrain*, pp. 222, 279.
The subject is taken from Virgil (*Æneid*, vii, 25).
Finished drawing closely connected with L.V.185, of which the painting, executed for Prince Gaspero Altieri in 1675, is in the Vanderbilt collection. Another drawing for the same composition is in the British Museum (Hind, 303), and is dated 1675.
The Windsor drawing only differs from the painting in small details and, since it is dated two years after the execution of the painting, it must represent a return to the theme by Claude. The drawing may have been intended to be complete in itself or it may be a preparation for a new painting.
Mrs. Pattison mentions another drawing of the same subject, in the Howard Sale, 1873, signed and dated 1673.

49. Landscape with trees and a bridge.   No. 13095.
96 mm. × 154 mm. Pen and bistre wash.
Literature: *Seventeenth Century Art*, R.A., 1938, p. 171, No. 502a.

An experiment in landscape composition, with three small figures. Not directly connected with any known painting, but related to compositions such as L.V.87, 147, and III, 99. Probably c. 1640–60. On the verso is a letter, not in Claude's handwriting, which in so far as it is decipherable reads as follows:

Molto . . . . . Charissimo Amico havremo Rcevuto le Charissime Lettere . . . . che lei à . . . . Il Sig^re Cavaliere Architetto Di Sua . . . . . P . . Pellic . . a (?) . . . havremo Grandissimo Gusto e Consolation(e) . . . . del (?) suo ben^e stare . . . . . . po Gratia Conforma, ha Azz . . . . . il Sig^re Architetto al Sig^re Claudio che V.S. fa opere G . . . . e Cond . . . magiormente il Sig^re Claudio . . . . . habbia occupatione al temp . . . . . ce sono . . . . . credimo che lei sta meglio l . . . . . . che in . . . . ogni Cosa e char . . . . aco lei di Sig . . . . . ed Altro per Cag . . . lata . . . . . e di . . . . .

B. Drawings from Nature.

The following twelve drawings, which are of almost exactly the same dimensions and very close in general character, probably formed part of a single notebook. Nos. 50–57 form a series of sketches of buildings in and near Rome, upright in format and all in pen and luminous bistre wash. Nos. 58 and 59 are similar in theme and format, but are conceived primarily in line. Nos. 60 and 61 are oblong landscapes without buildings, very free in handling. Two of the sheets, Nos. 50 and 56, have figure studies on the verso, in the case of No. 56 probably by another hand.

It is difficult to date exactly these sketches, but they come nearest to other similar work of the 'forties.

50. *Recto:* The wall of a villa near Rome.
Pl. 88. No. 13084.

127 mm. × 93 mm. Pen and bistre wash.

Literature: Chamberlaine, pl. 36.

Verso: Figure studies. Pen and bistre.

A group of three women talking, on the right a man, and indications of two other figures.

51. The Campo Vaccino with the entrance to the Villa Farnese. *Pl. 80.* No. 13085.

128 mm. × 94 mm. Pen and bistre wash.

Literature: Chamberlaine, pl. 44.

On the left, Vignola's gate to the Villa Farnese, now destroyed. In the background on the right the church of S. Maria Liberatrice built by Onofrio Lunghi, destroyed in this century to uncover the remains of the church of S. Maria Antiqua beneath it.

52. View of the Colosseum. *Pl. 85.* No. 13086.

125 mm. × 92 mm. Pen and bistre wash.

Literature: Chamberlaine, pl. 54.

A view of the upper part of the outer wall on the east side, seen from the top of the inner galleries.

53. View of the Colosseum. *Pl. 83.* No. 13088.

127 mm. × 92 mm. Pen and bistre wash.

Literature: Chamberlaine, pl. 33; *Grosvenor Gallery Publications*; *Seventeenth Century Art*, R.A., 1938, p. 169, No. 494a.

Apparently a view from one of the galleries on the south side of the Colosseum.

54. Roman arches and tower. *Pl. 81.* No. 13087.

127 mm. × 91 mm. Pen and bistre wash over black chalk.

Literature: Chamberlaine, pl. 53.

The exact subject cannot be identified, but it may be one of the gates in the ancient walls of Rome. On the left in the foreground, barely distinguishable, is a seated man drawing.

55. The Campo Vaccino with the Basilica of Constantine. *Pl. 82.* No. 13089.

128 mm. × 93 mm. Pen and bistre wash.

Literature: Chamberlaine, pl. 37; *Seventeenth Century Art*, R.A., 1938, p. 169, No. 494b.

The drawing represents the Basilica of Constantine, although it shows it with coffered half-domes instead of barrel vaulting. It is just possible, however, that Claude may have been drawing from memory.

56. *Recto:* S. Giorgio in Velabro. *Pl. 87.* No. 13090.

128 mm. × 95 mm. Pen and bistre wash.

Literature: Chamberlaine, pl. 34.

The porch and tower of the church seen from the south, with the Arcus Argentarium in front of the tower, and a corner of the Janus Quadrifrons on the extreme right. A different view of the Arcus Argentarium occurs in one of Claude's harbour scenes (L.V.19).

Verso: Study of a man leaning on a staff.
Red chalk.

A drawing of a nude, too skilful to be by Claude.

57. A house in the Campagna. *Pl. 89.* No. 13091.

127 mm. × 94 mm. Pen and bistre wash.

Literature: Chamberlaine, pl. 45; *Grosvenor Gallery Publications*.

58. SS. Giovanni e Paolo, Rome. *Pl. 84.* No. 13096.

127 mm. × 94 mm. Pen and bistre wash.

Literature: Chamberlaine, pl. 61; *Seventeenth Century Art*, R.A., 1938, p. 171, No. 502b.

Another drawing of the same church from a point nearer to the apse is L.V. III, 56, then in the collection of Charles Lambert.

59. An artist drawing. *Pl. 90.* No. 13092.

128 mm. × 93 mm. Pen and bistre.

Literature: Chamberlaine, pl. 60; *Grosvenor Gallery Publications*.

An artist sits on a wooden platform drawing a statue just visible between the columns of a classical portico on the left. Behind, another statue on a pedestal.

60. Landscape: a valley with trees.   *Pl. 91.* No. 13093.

92 mm. × 126 mm. Pen and bistre wash.

Literature: Chamberlaine, pl. 40.

This and the following drawing, No. 61, are probably both sketches from nature, but they are more elaborately designed than the other drawings from the same sketchbook, and perhaps represent a first stage towards a composition.

61. The banks of the Tiber.   *Pl. 92.* No. 13094.

92 mm. × 127 mm. Pen and bistre wash.

Literature: Chamberlaine, pl. 39.

See note on the preceding drawing, No. 60.

62. The Tomb of Cecilia Metella.   *Pl. 93.* No. 13078.

98 mm. × 223 mm. Black and red chalk, with grey wash.

Another drawing of the same subject is L.V. III, No. 58, then in the collection of Charles Lambert. Mrs. Pattison (*Claude Lorrain*, p. 248) mentions two others, one in the Albertina, and the other formerly in Jonathan Richardson's collection. These three drawings may, however, not all be distinct.

The technique of this drawing recalls the work of Silvestre. It is, however, too luminous and sensitive to be from his hand.

CLAUDE GELLEE, *Le Lorrain.* (Attributed to.)

63. *Recto:* A study of trees.   *Pl. 94.* No. 11927.

285 mm. × 221 mm. Pen and bistre, with black chalk.

Literature: Borenius, 'An Exhibition of Poussin and Claude Drawings', *Old Master Drawings*, iii, 1928, p. 18 and pl. 18 (as Poussin); *French Art*, R.A., 1932, p. 138, No. 689 (as Poussin).

Verso: The same study partly traced through.

Black chalk.

Hitherto attributed to Poussin, but certainly not by him. It does not, moreover, appear to come from either of the old collections of Poussin's drawings at Windsor, and the attribution is probably recent. The sketch on the recto is very close to certain drawings of trees by Claude, such as Nos. 41 and 43, verso above. The black chalk tracing through on the verso recalls Nos. 42 and 43. These parallels justify a tentative attribution to Claude.

64. View of S. Maria del Popolo, Rome.   No. 11999.

154 mm. × 255 mm. Oval. Pen and bistre wash on blue paper.

The drawing shows S. Maria del Popolo with the obelisk of the Piazza del Popolo and part of the walls of Rome, seen from the south.

It is traditionally attributed to Poussin, but is certainly not by him. The blue paper, the luminous wash and the thin delicate line, combined with a certain clumsiness in

the drawing of the trees, make an attribution to Claude plausible.

The drawing has suffered by being cut to an oval.

CLAUDE GELLEE, *Le Lorrain* (School of). (?Giovanni Domenico Desiderii, c. 1623–1667.)

65. *Recto:* Landscape with a bridge.   No. 5808.

202 mm. × 261 mm. Bistre wash over black chalk.

Literature: *Seventeenth Century Art*, R.A., 1938, p.167, No. 488. (Attributed to Poussin.)

Verso: Study of cows.

Bistre wash over black chalk.

66. Landscape with valley.   No. 5803.

190 mm. × 262 mm. Bistre wash over black chalk.

67. *Recto:* Roman ruins.   No. 5823.

123 mm. × 194 mm. Black chalk.

Verso: Landscape with a man driving cows.

Bistre wash over black chalk.

68. *Recto:* A rustic hut.   No. 5806.

116 mm. × 192 mm. Bistre wash over black chalk.

Verso: Another view of the same hut.

Bistre wash over black chalk.

These four drawings are all by the same hand. No. 65 has been exhibited with a tentative attribution to Nicolas Poussin, and the name of Grimaldi has also been suggested for it. It has, however, nothing to do with either of these artists, and is closer in general character to Claude, though it is too dry to be from his own hand. On the basis of a signed drawing by G. D. Desiderii (cf. *Burlington*, lvii, p. 111, pl. I A) this Italian imitator of Claude's seems the most likely author for this drawing and also, therefore, for the other three in the group.

CLAUDE GELLEE, *Le Lorrain* (School of).

69. Landscape with a view of a valley.   No. 13099.

279 mm. × 423 mm. Bistre wash.

A very free sketch in brush only. On the analogy of two drawings in the British Museum (reproduced in Friedlaender, *Claude Lorrain*, pp. 168, 176) this may be a weak original by Claude. But it is more likely to be the work of a close imitator.

70. Landscape with hut.   No. 5811.

203 mm. × 280 mm. Bistre wash over black chalk.

Probably by the same hand as No. 69.

71. Landscape with a tree and Egyptian ruins.

No. 13171.

188 mm. × 250 mm. Pen and bistre wash over black chalk.

Verso: A tree similar to that on the recto.

Black chalk.

The fantastic tree and the attempt to indicate an exotic type of architecture suggest that this may possibly have been a study for a composition of Jonah under the gourd outside Nineveh.

The use of wash is in the manner of Claude, but the drawing of the tree is so coarse that the whole composition must be the work of an imitator.

HENRI GISSEY (1621(?)–1673). (Attributed to.)

72. Louis XIV as Apollo. *Frontispiece.* No. 13071.

295 mm. × 216 mm. Water-colour with gold on vellum. Inscribed: *Apollon Le Roy.*

A design for a ballet costume of Apollo for the young Louis XIV. From the King's age it is evident that the drawing must be connected with one of the earliest ballets in which he took part. His first appearance was in *Cassandre* in 1651, but in this ballet he did not dance the part of Apollo. In the *Ballet de la Nuit*, produced in 1653 he appeared as Apollo, in a costume designed by Stefano della Bella, the drawing for which is preserved in the Bibliothèque Nationale (cf. Boehn, *Das Bühnenkostüm*, p. 301 and L. Dubech, *Histoire Générale Illustrée du Théâtre*, iii, p. 110). The present drawing agrees closely with the description given by Celler of the dress which he wore in the ballet in the *Noces de Thétis et de Pélée*, performed at the Petit Bourbon on January 26th, 1654, of which a drawing exists in the volume of the libretto in the Institut de France (cf. Celler, *Les décors, les costumes, et la mise en scène au 17ᵉ siècle*, pp. 90, 95, and Bapst, *Essai sur l'Histoire du Théâtre*, 1893, p. 239). Celler describes the costume as follows: 'Un maillot rose semble d'abord couvrir le corps; de hauts brodequins légers et brodés d'or et de pierres précieuses montent jusqu'aux genoux; le torse, depuis le menton jusqu'aux poignets, est couvert d'un pourpoint long et ajusté venant jusqu'à mi-cuisse, fait de mousseline toute brodée d'or, de diamants et de rubis; la tête, avec les cheveux blonds bouclés tombant sur les épaules, porte un diadème de rubis et de perles, d'où s'échappent des rayons d'or et de diamants avec d'énormes aigrettes de plumes blanches et jaunes.'

With the exception of one point of colour, namely that the tights in the drawing are white instead of pink, this account agrees exactly with the Windsor drawing. The Institut drawing is moreover reproduced in H. Prunières' edition of the *Œuvres Complètes de F. B. Lully, Les Ballets*, i, 1931, and a comparison with this reproduction proves definitely that the Windsor drawing is of the same costume, though the pose is somewhat different.

It is not known for certain who made the designs for the costumes for this ballet. The engravings in the volume illustrating the *Noces de Thétis et de Pélée*, published in 1654, are concerned with the setting and *machines* only, and the figures are not shown in the dresses which they actually wore (Apollo, for instance, is shown in the nude). The engravings are inscribed: *Francart del. I. Torelli in. I. Silvestre fecit.* Torelli was the inventor of the *machines*, Francart probably only made the drawings after the indications of Torelli, and Silvestre was the engraver.

By far the most likely candidate, however, as designer of the dresses is Henri Gissey, who was in 1654 'dessinateur ordinaire du Cabinet du Roi' and in charge of the dress designing for the Royal ballets. This attribution is supported by the likeness of the Windsor drawing to two sketches attributed to Gissey in the Victoria and Albert Museum. One, a project for a dress probably worn by Louis XIV (E 1310–1936), is similar in general conception and also in handling. The other, a rougher sketch of a dress for a dancer playing the part of Love (E 1300–1936), is much freer in technique but is again similar in general type. A further likeness is to be found in the water-colours for the *Courses de Testes et de Bague* of 1661 by Gissey in the Nationalbibliothek in Vienna (cf. *Denkmäler des Theaters*, Vienna, Nationalbibliothek, vi).

NICOLAS RAYMOND DE LA FAGE (1656–1690).

There are sixty-two drawings at Windsor by this prolific artist. Forty-six of these are described in the manuscript catalogue, which mentions seven more without stating what they represent. The remaining nine were found among the Italian drawings, without attribution. Almost all the drawings seem to have come from Italian collections, and it seems quite probable that they were executed during La Fage's visit to Rome in 1679–80.

73–112. Illustrations to the *Metamorphoses* of Ovid.

The manuscript catalogue mentions 'forty . . . designs taken from the *Metamorphosis* of Ovid'. This refers to the present series, thirty-eight of which are almost identical in size and technique, and bear similar inscriptions, the two remaining drawings (Nos. 111 and 112) being alternative designs for two of the main series (109 and 110), without inscriptions. All but three illustrate scenes from the *Metamorphoses*, the three exceptions being subjects from the story of Helen and Paris. The inscriptions give the subject of each drawing, together with the reference to the passage from which it is taken. These references, however, are given in terms of *fables*, not of *books* and *lines*. It seems, therefore, that La Fage was using one of the adaptations of Ovid in which the *Metamorphoses* were broken up into short fables, and certain stories added from other sources. No edition can be traced in which the numbering of the fables exactly corresponds to the references on the drawings, but those which most nearly satisfy the conditions are the French translations of Renouard (1617) and Du Ryer (1667), both of which were frequently reprinted during the seventeenth century, and in both of which the story of Paris and Helen is included.

It is possible that La Fage's drawings were made for a new translation into Italian which was never published. The inscriptions are in Italian, and not in La Fage's own hand. They appear to have been added by a writer who was not a reliable classical scholar, for in several instances he makes mistakes of name. In drawing No. 109, for instance, he confuses *Alcide* with *Aci*, and in No. 108 he describes the subject as the Sacrifice of Polyxena, whereas it is certainly that of Iphigenia. In addition to the main inscription at the top of the drawings, some of them have a second inscription, in a fainter writing, at the bottom, in general merely a repetition of the text at the top in shorter form. This second series of legends has not been copied in the following entries.

All the drawings are approximately 200 mm. × 267 mm. They are in pen and bistre with grey-blue wash, a favourite technique with La Fage. Some have traces of black chalk, and in most of them the composition is framed in lightly ruled black chalk lines. The drawings all seem to have been numbered in the top right-hand corner, though in some cases the number has been cut off, together with parts of the inscriptions. It seems likely that the whole series was intended to be engraved, but there is no evidence that this project was ever carried out. The first drawing is signed: *Lafage invenit*. The fact that the inscriptions are all in Italian strengthens the theory that they were probably made in Rome.

73. The Creation of the World. No. 6192.
Numbered: 2. Inscribed: *Creatione del Mondo*. Signed: *Lafage invenit*.
Met., i, 32.

74. The Creation of Man. No. 6193.
Numbered: 3. Inscribed: *Prometo dà la Vita Alhuomo col fuoco robato dal ciello favola 2.3.4.*
Met., i, 76.

75. The Golden Age. No. 6194.
Inscription cut off.
Met., i, 90.

76. The Destruction of the Giants. No. 6195.
Numbered: 5. Inscribed: *Giove fulmina y Giganti—favola 6.*
Met., i, 151.

77. Lycaon transformed into a wolf. No. 6196.
Inscription cut off.
Met., i, 226.

78. The Deluge. No. 6197.
Inscribed: *Il Diluvio favola 8.*
Met., i, 262.

79. Deucalion and Pyrrha. No. 6198.
Inscribed: *Deucalion . . . . .*
Met., i, 395.

80. The Sisters of Phaethon transformed into willows. No. 6199.
Numbered: 9. Inscribed: *Le Sorelle di Fetonte favola. 14.*
Met., ii, 340.

81. Cygnus transformed into a swan. No. 6200.
Numbered: 10. Inscribed: *Cigno Re di Liguria—favola comme prima 14.*
Met., ii, 367.

82. The rape of Europa. No. 6201.
Numbered: 11. Inscribed: *Europa rapita da Giove. favola 21.*
Met., ii, 873.

83. Cadmus killing the dragon. No. 6202.
Numbered: 12. Inscribed: *Cadmo fratello di Europa. favola—22.*
Met., iii, 55.

84. Diana and Actæon. No. 6204.
Numbered: 13. Inscribed: *Atheone favola. 24.*
Met., iii, 193.

85. Narcissus. No. 6205.
Numbered: 14. Inscribed: *Narciso favola—27.*
Met., iii, 413.

86. Pyramus and Thisbe. No. 6206.
Numbered: 1(5). Inscribed: *Piramo e Tisbe. favola—31.*
Met., iv, 95.

87. Perseus killing Medusa. No. 6207.
Numbered: 16. Inscribed: *Medusa—favola—37.*
Met., iv, 776.

88. Perseus and Andromeda. No. 6203.
Inscribed: *Andromeda . . . .*
Met., iv, 672. Another drawing of this subject by La Fage exists at Windsor, cf. No. 116.

89. The Rape of Proserpine. No. 6208.
Numbered: 18. Inscribed: *Plutone e Proserpina—favola—39.*
Met., v, 391. Another drawing of this subject by La Fage exists at Windsor, cf. No. 118.

90. Diana and Endymion. No. 6209.
Numbered: 19. Inscribed: *Andimione (?) favola. 45.*
This story is not mentioned by Ovid.

91. The Daughters of Niobe.   No. 6210.
Numbered: 20. Inscribed: *Niobe favola—48.*
Met., vi. 273.

92. Apollo and Marsyas.   No. 6211.
Numbered: 21. Inscribed: *Apollo e Marsia—favola. 50.*
Met., vi, 382.

93. Jason and Medea.   No. 6213.
Numbered: 2(2). Inscribed: *Giasone e Meda, favolae 52.*
Met., vii, 74.

94. Jason and the Bulls.   No. 6212.
Numbered: 23. Inscribed: *Giasone comme prima 52.*
Met., vii, 100.

95. Daedalus and Icarus.   No. 6214.
Numbered: 24. Inscribed: *Dedalo e Icara favola 61.*
Met., viii, 183.

96. Venus and Adonis.   No. 6215.
Numbered: 25. Inscribed: *Adone—favola 64.*
Met., x, 529.

97. Hercules killing the Hydra.   No. 6216.
Numbered: 26. Inscribed: *Le Virtu di Hercule favola 66.*
Met., ix, 192.

98. Hercules, Iole and Eurytus.   No. 6217.
Inscribed: *Hercole et Iole—favola—67.*
Hercules' love for Iole is only referred to by Ovid (*Met.*, ix, 140) but is described in greater detail by **other** ancient writers (e.g. Apollodorus, ii, 6, 1).

99. Hercules and Antæus.   No. 6218.
Numbered: 28. Inscribed: *Hercole et Acheloo—68.*
The inscription identifies the subject incorrectly. The drawing shows Hercules conquering Antæus by lifting him up so that he was no longer in contact with his mother, the Earth, who was the source of his strength. (cf. *Met.*, ix, 184).

100. Hercules, Nessus and Deianira.   No. 6219.
Numbered: 29. Inscribed: *Hercole e Nesso favola comme prima 68.*
Met., ix, 101.

101. The Death of Hercules.   No. 6220.
Numbered: 30. Inscribed: *La Morte di Hercole favola 69.*
Met., ix, 299.

102. The Death of Eurydice.   No. 6221.
Numbered: 31. Inscribed: *Euridice moglie di Orfeo—favola 71.*
Met., x, 8.

103. Eurydice carried back to Hades. No. 2622.
Numbered: 32. Inscribed: *Orfé perse l'Euridice favola 72.*
Met., x, 56. Another drawing of this subject by La Fage exists at Windsor, cf. No. 117.

104. Alcyone finding the body of Ceyx. No. 6223.
Numbered: 33. Inscribed: *Ceice e Alcione favola 79.*
Met., xi, 725.

105. The Judgment of Paris.   No. 6224.
Numbered: 34. Inscribed: *Il Giudice di Paride favola 80.*
Not mentioned in Ovid.

106. The Rape of Helen.   *Pl. III.* No. 6225.
Numbered: 35. Inscribed: *Il Rapo di Helena favola 81.*
A subject not described by Ovid.

107. Æneas taking leave of Dido (?). No. 6226.
Numbered: 36. Inscribed: *Il Rapo di Helena favola 81.*
The inscription wrongly identifies the subject as the Rape of Helen. It clearly represents a scene of parting. From the position of the drawing in the series it should represent one of the Greek heroes leaving for the Trojan War, but it conforms to the more popular story of Dido and Æneas, and may have originally been placed elsewhere in the series.

108. The Sacrifice of Iphigenia.   No. 6227.
Numbered: 37. Inscribed: *Il Sacrificio di Polissena favola 82.*
Wrongly described in the Italian text. The fact that the victim is being carried off by Diana, and a hind substituted for her proves that the subject is the sacrifice of Iphigenia, not that of Polyxena (cf. *Met.*, xii, 28).

109. Polyphemus, Acis and Galatea.   No. 6230.
Numbered: 38. Inscribed: *Polifemo e Alcide favola 83.*
Met., xiii, 876. The Italian text has *Alcide* instead of *Aci.* An alternative drawing for the subject is also at Windsor, cf. No. 111 below.

110. Polyphemus wooing Galatea.   No. 6228.
Numbered: 39. Inscribed: *Polifemo a Galatea favola 84.*
Met., xiii, 738. In the logical sequence this drawing should come before No. 109, but it is numbered to come after it. An alternative drawing of the subject is also at Windsor, cf. No. 112 below.

111. **Polyphemus, Acis and Galatea.** *Pl. 113.* No. 6231.

165 mm. × 246 mm. Pen and bistre with grey-blue wash.

Closely related to No. 109 above, but not actually belonging to the series, since it has neither number nor inscription. The figure of Polyphemus is almost identical in both drawings.

112. **Polyphemus wooing Galatea.**   No. 6229.

167 mm. × 258 mm. Pen and bistre with grey-blue wash.

Like No. 111 above a variant for the Ovid series, but not directly related to the other drawing of the same subject (No. 110 above).

———————

113. **Self-portrait.**   *Pl. 112.* No. 6185.

194 mm. × 261 mm. Pen and bistre with grey-blue wash.

Signed: *Raymont Lafage ivenit.*

The artist is shown in an oval frame, crowned with vine leaves, and holding a pen in his right hand and reaching down to a jar of wine with his left. On the right Bacchus sits on a wine-barrel, holding a glass of wine, and behind him in the distance is a Bacchic scene. On the left the figure of painting with pen, palette and brushes. Behind her, in the distance, Pegasus.

Probably intended as the frontispiece to a series of drawings to one of the lighter classical poets. The size and technique suggest that it may have belonged to the series of illustrations to Ovid, of which the first is missing. Other similar allegorical self-portraits by La Fage are known (e.g. Louvre 5408, and others recorded in engravings).

114. **Mercury and Argus.**   No. 6189.

237 mm. × 380 mm. Pen and bistre with grey-blue wash. Inscribed: *di Monsù la Fage* in an eighteenth-century Italian handwriting.

In the foreground Argus falls alseep under the influence of Mercury's piping. In the background Mercury carries the head of Argus to Juno.

115. **Hercules and the Nemean Lion.**   No. 6188.

252 mm. × 332 mm. Pen and bistre with grey-blue wash. Inscribed: *di Monsù lafage* in an eighteenth-century Italian handwriting.

116. **Perseus and Andromeda.**   No. 3825a.

172 mm. × 209 mm. Triangular. Pen and bistre with grey-blue wash.

A pair to No. 117.

Another drawing by La Fage of the same subject is No. 88. This and the following seven drawings were without attribution among the Italian drawings, but are evidently by La Fage.

117. **Eurydice carried back to Hades.**   No. 3825b.

178 mm. × 210 mm. Triangular. Pen and bistre with grey-blue wash.

A pair to No. 116. Another drawing by La Fage of the same subject is No. 103.

118. **The Rape of Proserpine.**   No. 3828b.

112 mm. × 214 mm. Triangular. Pen and bistre with grey-blue wash.

A pair to No. 119. Another drawing of this subject by La Fage is No. 89.

119. **Unidentified mythological subject.** No. 3828a.

114 mm. × 214 mm. Triangular. Pen and bistre with grey-blue wash.

The drawing depicts a bearded man resting on the back of a bull enveloped in clouds. Above a goddess and wind-god. In the right foreground a river-god, and in the distance a town with pyramids.

A pair to No. 118.

120. **Spring.**   No. 3826a.

130 mm. × 160 mm. Triangular. Pen and bistre with grey-blue wash.

121. **Summer.**   No. 3827a.

95 mm. × 256 mm. Triangular. Pen and bistre with grey-blue wash.

122. **Autumn.**   No. 3826b.

131 mm. × 160 mm. Triangular. Pen and bistre with grey-blue wash.

123. **Winter.**   No. 3827b.

96 mm. × 255 mm. Triangular. Pen and bistre with grey-blue wash.

These four drawings, all triangular in form, two upright and two oblong, appear to form a series, probably intended as designs for decorative engravings.

124. **Lot and his daughters.**   No. 6184.

172 mm. × 260 mm. Pen and bistre. Inscribed on the eighteenth-century mount: *Mutia la Faigli.*

A drawing of this subject by La Fage is described in the manuscript catalogue.

The inscription on the mount is in a hand which occurs on many Italian drawings at Windsor, and indicates that the drawing came from an Italian collection.

125. **The Israelites crossing the Red Sea.**   No. 6840.

403 mm. × 556 mm. Pen and bistre.

126. The Israelites collecting the Manna.　No. 6841.

407 mm. × 575 mm. Pen and bistre.

Presumably identical with two drawings by La Fage, 'Pharaoh and his Host drowned', and 'The Children of Israel fed by Manna', mentioned in the manuscript catalogue in one of the volumes of 'large drawings' entitled 'Opere Varie'. The Italian title to the volume, as well as the other contents, suggest that they were bought in Italy. Both drawings are strongly Poussinesque in conception, but typical of La Fage in the vigorous and rather coarse draughtsmanship.

127. The Denial of St. Peter.　No. 6181.

136 mm. × 168 mm. Pen and bistre over black chalk.

128. The Denial of St. Peter.　No. 6182.

147 mm. × 170 mm. Pen and bistre.

Presumably the two drawings by La Fage described as 'St. Peter denying Christ' in the manuscript catalogue. The composition of both these drawings recalls the French followers of Caravaggio, but the draughtsmanship is that of La Fage.

129. Tancred baptising Clorinda.　No. 3829.

133 mm. × 205 mm. Pen and bistre with grey-blue wash.

The subject is taken from Tasso, *Gerusalemme Liberata*, xii, v. 66. From the unattributed Italian drawings.

130. A Battle.　No. 6328.

326 mm. × 510 mm. Pen and bistre over black chalk. Inscribed in an eighteenth-century hand: *Lafage*.

131. A Battle.　*Pl. 114*. No. 6329.

366 mm. × 449 mm. Pen and bistre wash over black chalk. In lower right-hand corner figures 99 (struck out) and 171.

132. Unidentified subject.　No. 6190.

215 mm. × 147 mm. Pen and Indian ink.

Two figures lift up a dead body of a warrior, whose shield and weapons are indicated on the ground.

133. Study of an Angel.　No. 6183.

182 mm. × 245 mm. Pen, Indian ink and black chalk.

Presumably the drawing by La Fage described as 'An Angel' in the manuscript catalogue. An exact copy of a drawing in the Ashmolean Museum (Robinson, 1870, p. 233, No. 94) formerly attributed to Raphael, and connected with the Sacrifice of Isaac on the ceiling of the Sala d'Eliodoro.

134. A sheet of studies.　No. 6191.

157 mm. × 248 mm. Pen and bistre with grey-blue wash.

The studies include two galloping horses, a running dog, a wine jar and a basket of clothes.

LAURENT DE LA HYRE (1606–1656).

135. The Adoration of the Shepherds.　*Pl. 100*. No. 0184.

432 mm. × 265 mm. Black chalk on buff paper. Cut and mended at the top.

A finished study, with only slight variations, for the painting in the museum at Rouen (reproduced in Dimier and Réau, *Histoire de la Peinture française*, 1627–1690, i, pl. 27).

The drawing seems originally to have been rounded at the top, but most of the arched part has been cut off and the small remaining corners filled in.

CHARLES LEBRUN (1619–1690).

136. Portrait of the Duc de Roquelaure.　No. 13072.

380 mm. × 258 mm. Black chalk and Indian ink wash. Inscribed: *C le Brun f.*

The subject of this portrait is traditionally identified as Gaston Jean Baptiste, duc de Roquelaure, marshal of France (1617–1683). The dress indicates a date about 1655–60, and the style of the drawing agrees with Lebrun's manner at about that date.

The duc de Roquelaure appears in Lebrun's composition of the Capture of Dôle from the tapestries 'Les Conquêtes du Roi', woven 1672–76. Portraits of him are also known engraved by Mariette and Trouvain.

137. Study for the head of a Persian.　*Pl. 110*. No. 5167.

369 mm. × 250 mm. Black chalk.

Study for the head of a Persian fleeing in terror in the painting of 'The Battle of Arbela' from the Alexander series executed between 1660 and 1668 (Louvre, No. 510).

The psychological interest which the artist here displays in the effect of terror on the human face links this drawing closely to his studies for the *Méthode pour apprendre à dessiner les Passions*, published in 1667, the drawings for which are in the Louvre (6447–6509).

SEBASTIEN LECLERC (1637–1714).

137a. The Siege of Orsoy.　*Military Costumes*, v, p. 15.

211 mm. × 264 mm. Pen and Indian ink with some water colour. Inscribed: *Le Clerc*.

137b. The Siege of Burick.　*Military Costumes*, v, p. 15.

205 mm. × 262 mm. Pen and Indian ink.

Nos. 137a and 137b are exact studies for the engravings by Chastillon for the *Petites Conquêtes de Louis XIV*.

EUSTACHE LE SUEUR (1617–1655).

The eighteenth-century manuscript catalogue lists twelve drawings by Le Sueur in a mixed volume containing four drawings attributed to Poussin, and others by French seventeenth-century artists. All those attributed to Le Sueur can be identified with reasonable probability, though one of them, No. 6174, Venus and Adonis, is not mentioned in the present catalogue on the grounds that it is not by Le Sueur but probably by an Italian artist of the seventeenth century. Another, No. 342, is by Bernard Picart. Nothing is known about the provenance of the three drawings, Nos. 139, 141, 142.

138. The Angel leaving Tobit.   *Pl. 106.* No. 6168.

225 mm. × 183 mm. Black chalk. Inscribed in an eighteenth-century hand: *Le Sueur.*

Probably the drawing described in the manuscript catalogue as 'The Angel leaving Manoah' (but cf. also No. 143 verso). It cannot, however, represent this subject since there is no sacrifice represented, although iconographically it derives from representations of the story of Manoah. Moreover it is clearly a study for the painting in the museum at Grenoble (No. 68) of the Angel leaving Tobit, probably painted for M. Fieubet (cf. *Mémoires Inédits*, i, p. 157, and *French Art*, R.A., 1932, p. 31, No. 109, and pl. 28). The painting is a fairly early work, about 1640–45, with traces of the influence of Vouet, and the drawing must belong to the same period.

139. The Return of the Holy Family from the Temple.
                                      Pl. 107. No. 6172.

202 mm. × 145 mm. Black chalk. Inscribed in an eighteenth-century hand: *Le Sueur.*

Study for a stained glass window erected by Perrier after Le Sueur's design, and engraved in Landon (pl. 18) when the window was in the Musée des Petits Augustins. Surprisingly enough Le Sueur seems to have been inspired by Rubens' composition, which he could have known from engravings.

140. The Assumption of the Virgin. *Pl. 103.* No. 6175.

161 mm. × 230 mm. Black chalk. Squared. Inscribed in an eighteenth-century hand: *Le Sueur.*

Mentioned in the manuscript catalogue. Probably a study for the painting executed for M. Brissonet and now lost (cf. *Mémoires Inédits*, i, p. 164).

141. The Ecstasy of St. Paul.   *Pl. 108.* No. 6173.

270 mm. × 252 mm. Black chalk. Squared. Inscribed in an eighteenth-century hand: *Le Sueur.*

No painting of this subject by Le Sueur is recorded. The composition is based on Poussin's two versions of the subject, which in their turn are imitations of Raphael's 'Vision of Ezekiel'. Poussin's versions were painted in 1643 and 1650, for patrons in Paris, and Le Sueur

presumably knew both. A somewhat similar group occurs in the last painting in the series illustrating the life of St. Bruno, showing 'St. Bruno carried up to Heaven' (Louvre, No. 585).

The severe classical style of the drawing indicates that it was executed in the last years of Le Sueur's life, probably 1650–55.

142. The Muses Clio, Euterpe and Thalia.
                                      Pl. 105. No. 6171.

145 mm. × 156 mm. Black chalk. Squared. Inscribed in an eighteenth-century hand: *Le Sueur.*

Exact study, in reverse, for the painting executed for the Cabinet des Muses in the Hôtel Lambert, and now in the Louvre (No. 598), probably executed about 1650–55. The fact that the drawing is in reverse suggests that it may have been made for an engraving, but its style is so exactly that of Le Sueur's preliminary sketches that it must be regarded as an original. A drawing for the figure of Clio, in the same sense as the painting, but less close to it in the pose of the head, is in the Louvre (No. 9158).

143. *Recto:* The Birth of Minerva.   No. 6169.

170 mm. × 260 mm. Black chalk. Squared. Inscribed in an eighteenth-century hand: *Tournes*(?). *naisence de minerve. le Sueur.*

Probably the drawing described in the manuscript catalogue as: 'Jupiter, Juno, Minerva, etc.'

The drawing is somewhat obscure, owing to the superimposition of several schemes for the composition. The final design, the extent of which is shown by the area squared, comprises three figures. On the left sits Jupiter, recognizable by the attributes of eagle and thunderbolt. Beside him stands Vulcan, who according to Hesiod, split open Jupiter's head from which sprang Minerva. Below to the right is Minerva, leaning on a sphere. In the background is a part of the Zodiac.

The preliminary schemes are indicated by the existence of another Minerva, slightly to the left of the final figure, and a Jupiter in reverse, on the extreme right. Next to this Jupiter appears another figure, not identifiable, but perhaps intended for Vulcan.

No painting is known of this composition. The squaring suggests that one must have been executed, but there is reason to think that Le Sueur often used squaring at an early stage in the evolution of a design, in preparation for a more finished drawing rather than for a painting.

Verso: Study for the Sacrifice of Manoah.
Black chalk.

Probably for the painting executed for M. du Lis mentioned by Florent le Comte (cf. Dussieux, 'Nouvelles Recherches sur la Vie et les Ouvrages de Le Sueur', *Archives de l'Art Français*, ii, 1852–53, p. 115) which may be either of two canvases in the museums of Toulouse or Caen.

144. The Gods of Olympus. *Pl. 104.* No. 6176.

160 mm. × 252 mm. Black chalk. Squared in red chalk. Inscribed in an eighteenth-century hand: *Le Sueur*.

Hebe hands the nectar to Jupiter. Other gods and goddesses are shown seated on clouds, but too roughly indicated to be identifiable.

Probably the drawing described in the manuscript catalogue as 'A Hero received by Jupiter and the heathen deitys'.

Not connected with any known composition, but similar in general character to those in the Cabinet de l'Amour at the Hôtel Lambert, and probably about the same date, i.e. 1645.

145. Theseus finding his father's sword. No. 6170.

187 mm. × 184 mm. Black chalk. Inscribed in an eighteenth-century hand: *Teseé leve la Pier qui cache lepeé de son pere.*

Mentioned in the manuscript catalogue.

This subject was popularized by Poussin (cf. Grautoff, Nos. 75, 76). The group of Aethra and the servant on whom she leans is based on Poussin's version, but the composition is even closer to the latter's 'Finding of Moses' (Grautoff, No. 77) of the same period as the 'Theseus', which includes a figure very like the crouching attendant in the drawing. No painting by Le Sueur of this subject is recorded.

146. Study of a priest holding a mitre. *Pl. 109.* No. 6166.

394 mm. × 211 mm. Black chalk on buff paper.

This drawing and Nos. 147–149 may compose the 'Four of Saints' mentioned in the manuscript catalogue.

Probably connected with a drawing in the Louvre (9275) which shows the same figure in a slightly different pose. The Louvre drawing is a study for the ninth painting in the series from the Life of St. Bruno, which depicts 'St. Bruno at the feet of St. Hugh' (Louvre, No. 572). In the painting, however, little survives from the Windsor sketch which must represent a first experiment for this figure. In Louvre 9275 the pose is altered, and the action of holding the mitre is then eliminated in a further study (Louvre 9277), which is followed exactly in the painting. In the last study and the painting the priest holds a broad-brimmed episcopal hat, not a mitre. About 1645–48.

147. Study of a figure in classical dress. No. 6164.

304 mm. × 160 mm. Black chalk on buff paper.

148. Study of a figure holding a book. No. 6165.

389 mm. × 220 mm. Black chalk on buff paper. Inscribed in an eighteenth-century hand: *Le Sueur*.

These two drawings are very similar in style to No. 146, but they do not appear to be connected with any known painting.

149. Three studies. No. 6167.

241 mm. × 369 mm. Black chalk on buff paper, heightened with white.

The sheet contains sketches of an old man with arm raised, another head of an old man, and the head and hand of a young man. All three figures are looking upwards in surprise, and probably belong to a composition such as the Ascension or the Assumption. They cannot, however, be related to any known painting.

150. A study of the head and shoulders of a man. No. 6163.

309 mm. × 200 mm. Black chalk on buff paper, heightened with white chalk. Inscribed in an eighteenth-century hand: *Le Sueur*.

Probably the drawing mentioned in the manuscript catalogue as: 'A head'. Similar in technique to Le Sueur's figure studies, but unusually naturalistic and vigorous. If it is actually by Le Sueur it must date from the period 1640–45 when he was shaking off the influence of Vouet but had not yet fully accepted the classical formula of Poussin.

ROBERT NANTEUIL (1623–1678). (After).

151. Portrait of the chancellor Michel Le Tellier (1603–1685). No. 5187.

242 mm. × 213 mm. Black and white chalk on grey-blue paper. Inscribed in an eighteenth-century hand: *Monsr. Mignard.*

A copy of Nanteuil's engraving of Le Tellier after a painting by Philippe de Champaigne, apparently lost. The eighteenth-century attribution to Mignard cannot be maintained since the drawing has no relation to his work.

GABRIEL PERELLE (1603–1677).

152. Landscape. *Pl. 96.* No. 13098.

102 mm. × 200 mm. Pen and bistre.

The attribution to Perelle is based on the close similarity to his engraved landscapes in composition, and to his pen drawings in handling.

FRANÇOIS PERRIER (1590–1650).

153. Design for the title page of the *Segmenta nobilium signarum et statuarum*. No. 6762.

233 mm. × 159 mm. Pen and bistre with grey wash over pencil. Inscribed with a long Latin dedication to the Marquis de Liancourt, whose arms appear above, signed: *Franciscus Perrier D.D.D. mdcxxxviii.* Below is the inscription: *Franciscus Perrier Burgund: delin. et sculp: Romae, superior, licentia. 1638.*

An exact preparation for the title page to the volume of engravings after ancient statues which Perrier published in Paris in 1638.

The composition shows Time gnawing at a piece of ancient sculpture (the Belvedere Torso), while below is the serpent eating its own tail (the symbol of eternity). The artist's theme is presumably that though time may destroy works of art, they may be preserved by means of drawings or engravings after them.

NICOLAS POUSSIN (1594–1665).

The drawings by Poussin and his school at Windsor form the most remarkable series of its kind in existence. They amount to 131 in all, and come in the main from two sources, both connected with the immediate circle of the artist himself. All but a few of them were till the second half of the last century bound in two volumes, which are now broken up but which can be almost completely reconstructed. The first of these volumes belonged to Cardinal Camillo Massimi, one of Poussin's best patrons in his later years, and was accompanied by a manuscript catalogue still in the library at Windsor. The history of this volume has been traced by Dr. Walter Friedlaender in his articles in the *Burlington Magazine* (LIV, 1929, pp. 116, 252), and his conclusions need only be repeated here with small additions and modifications. The core of the volume is formed by a series of drawings made for Poussin's earliest patron, the poet Marino, in Paris between the years 1620 and 1623. On his death in 1625 Marino bequeathed the drawings to the circle of his friends in Rome, probably to Poussin's friend and most regular patron, Cassiano del Pozzo. Almost all the other drawings in the volume date from the period 1624 to 1640 before Poussin's visit to Paris. Only seven drawings probably date from the period after his return to Rome in 1642. This is evidence that the collection was not primarily formed by Cardinal Massimi, with whom Poussin was not in touch before the end of the 'thirties but by Cassiano himself. On the other hand, we know that the volume belonged to Cardinal Massimi by 1650, for Félibien saw it in his possession in Rome, which he only visited between 1647 and 1650. This indicates that Cassiano must have given or sold the book to Massimi before his death in 1657, and not bequeathed it to him, as Friedlaender believed. Bellori saw it in the Cardinal's library and describes it as being there in his *Vite*, published in 1672. Cardinal Massimi died in 1677, and bequeathed all his possessions—and his debts—to his younger brother Fabio Camillo, who died in 1686. It was probably he who caused the manuscript catalogue to be made. This catalogue was written after the death of the Cardinal but before the end of the century, for it is mentioned in the catalogue that he died 'in this century'. The catalogue has on it a heraldic coat in which are the arms of Massimi, quartering a coat consisting of Colonna impaling Giustiniani. These arms could be those of either brother, since their maternal grandmother was a Giustiniani and their paternal great-grandmother a Colonna. On the other hand they are unlikely to be the arms of the presumed next owner. For Fabio Camillo had only one daughter, Giulia, who married Giovanni

Battista Massimi, a member of a different branch of the family, who was only descended from the Giustiniani and the Colonna through his mother.

It is not known for certain how the volume came from Rome to the Royal collection, but there is a strong probability that it was bought by Dr. Mead in Rome during his visit in 1695–96. It is known that Dr. Mead bought drawings from the Massimi collection, and also that Frederick, Prince of Wales, made purchases from Dr. Mead. The Massimi Poussins were in any case at Windsor by the end of the eighteenth century, when they were listed, together with the drawings in the other volume, in the manuscript catalogue of the Royal collection. One drawing mentioned in the seventeenth century catalogue was already missing at that date, but all the rest are still traceable at Windsor, the few which Friedlaender was unable to find having been rediscovered in the last few years and identified from the descriptions given by Woodward, the Royal librarian, in his articles in the *Fine Arts Quarterly Review* for 1863–64, written before the volumes were broken up.

One further point about the Massimi collection remains mysterious. The seventeenth-century catalogue is headed 'Alli Studiosi della Pittura Gio. Battista Marinella Armengol'.' The identity of the author has not hitherto been established. Friedlaender assumes his name to be Armengol, but the fact that the word is written *Armengol'* with an apostrophe in the Italian, and *Armengol:* with a colon in the English title-page suggests that it is an abbreviation, perhaps for *Armengolensis*, an indication of the birthplace of the author, whose name would then be Giovanni Battista Marinella. Moreover the word *Armengol:* in the English version is written in italics whereas the other parts of the name are written in ordinary script, which confirms the view that it is not part of the name proper. In fact a Giovanni Battista Marinella was librarian to the Pozzo family at the end of the seventeenth century (cf. J. Lumbroso, *Notizie sulla vita di Cassiano del Pozzo*, Turin, 1875, p. 44), and this must undoubtedly be our author. In any case, however, he was not a man of great originality, since both his general æsthetic introduction and his descriptions of the drawings are taken in great part word for word from Bellori, the former from the *Idea* with which he prefaced his *Vite*, and the latter from the *Vite* themselves. In some cases, indeed, when Bellori is describing a composition which is close to a Massimi drawing but not identical with it, the author of the catalogue follows Bellori too well, and his description does not agree with the details of the actual drawing (cf. below, No. 217). The English title-page reads: 'Description of Poussin's Original Designs and Sketches, writ by Giov. Battista Marinella Armengol: One of his Scholars: From the Cabinet of Cardinal Maximi'. Both the archaic form *writ* and the handwriting suggest that this inscription must date from the early eighteenth century, and it is probably, therefore, the title added by Dr. Mead.

Owing to its direct connection with the circle of Poussin, the Massimi volume can be expected to contain only drawings closely related to the artist. It does not on the other hand follow that all its contents will be original works by the master himself. Collectors of the seventeenth century did not attach great importance to the distinction between originals, copies and studio works, and we shall frequently find occasion to classify as derivative works drawings which were included in the Massimi volume on the ground that they represented in their general composition the ideas of Poussin.

The history of the other volume of Poussin drawings is less certain. The contents of the volume can be largely reconstructed from the late eighteenth century manuscript catalogue and from Woodward's account (it is referred to as 'II' in the following catalogue entries). Unfortunately, however, the latter is incomplete, and the third of his articles, which deals with this volume, breaks off after drawing number 15. The series of articles was never completed, but the manuscript catalogue gives some indication of a part of the remaining drawings. It ends, however, with a note added in the nineteenth century to the effect that the volume included thirteen drawings on five pages which are not described; and, further, some of the entries are too vague for it to be possible to identify the drawings intended.

The volume itself is almost certainly, as Friedlaender pointed out, the one which Winckelmann saw in 1759 in the library of Cardinal Alessandro Albani, of which he was curator (cf. Justi, *Winckelmann*, ii, p. 292). The whole of the Cardinal's collection of drawings and engravings was bought for George III in 1762 by the architect James Adam (cf. Justi, *op. cit.*, p. 306), and not by Dalton as suggested by Woodward. It is, moreover, extremely likely, as proposed by Friedlaender, that the contents came largely from the collection of Cassiano del Pozzo, like those of the Massimi volume. Cardinal Albani's uncle, Clement XI, who formed the collection of drawings, bought many of them from Cassiano del Pozzo's heir, Cosimo Antonio del Pozzo, in 1703 (cf. Premoli, article in *Arcadia*, 1918). According to Jouanny (*Correspondance de Nicolas Poussin*, Paris 1911, p. ix), letters to Cassiano also belonged to the Albani. The drawings themselves confirm the connection with Cassiano. One drawing, in fact, the sketch for the 'Agony in the Garden', probably for a painting belonging to Cassiano, was cut in two pieces, of which one was in the Massimi and the other in the Albani volume. They have now been reunited at Windsor. Moreover there are other close links with Cassiano. A sketch for the 'Confirmation' (No. 205) is a preliminary for the painting executed for him as part of the series of the Seven Sacraments; another, No. 263, of an ancient relief, has on it a number which corresponds to those on other drawings after the antique in the Albani collection, which appear to have belonged to Cassiano; others, such as No. 266, a sketch for 'Christ healing the Blind Men', No. 210, a study for

'Moses and the daughters of Jethro', and No. 251, 'Scipio and the Pirates', are for compositions for which other sketches exist in the Massimi volume. Moreover, the Scipio drawing is almost certainly that made for Cardinal Francesco Barberini, to whom Cassiano was secretary, and from whom he may well have received it as a gift. Finally, the volume contains a series of studio drawings dating from Poussin's visit to Paris in 1640–42, which he may have sent to Cassiano, since it is known from Poussin's letters that he kept Cassiano fully informed during the visit about his activities in Paris, and promised to send him from there drawings connected with the works on which he was engaged (*Correspondance*, pp. 57, 61). Another drawing of the same kind, No. 246, was in the Massimi volume.

In addition to the two volumes just discussed there were two others which contained a few drawings attributed to Poussin, the origins of which are entirely unknown. One (referred to as 'III' in the catalogue entries) included two school pieces (Nos. 278, 280,) and a drawing (11926) attributed to Poussin, but probably by Mola; and the other a few doubtful landscapes which cannot be identified.

There remain, however, certain drawings attributed to Poussin which cannot be traced to these volumes, some of which no doubt formed part of them and are those not described in the catalogue. In addition it would appear that some have been removed from the volumes and are probably now elsewhere in the Royal collection. It is likely, however, that nothing of great importance has disappeared, and it may well be that the drawings were quite properly removed when the volumes were broken up, on the ground that the attributions to Poussin were false.

Finally mention must be made of one group the origin of which also is unknown, namely the series of illustrations to the *Trattato* of Leonardo da Vinci (Nos. 230–245). The problems which they represent are discussed below in the catalogue entry devoted to them.

In the following catalogue of Poussin's drawings the order followed has been, as far as possible, one of date. It has been divided into sections corresponding to the main stages of the artist's career, and within these sections the individual drawings have been arranged according to what seems the most probable sequence of production.

A. The Marino Drawings.

Bellori (*Vite*, p. 9) tells us that when the Cavaliere Marino was in Paris he commissioned a series of drawings from Poussin. He adds that some of these drawings belonged to Cardinal Massimi, and describes one of them, 'The Birth of Adonis', in such detail that it can with certainty be identified with No. 154 below. On the basis of this drawing eight others (Nos. 155–162) almost identical in style, size and technique, all illustrating very similar mythological subjects, and all belonging to the

Massimi volume can be picked out as also belonging to the series executed for Marino.

Four other Massimi drawings (Nos. 165–168) almost identical in size, technique and style, but representing battle scenes from early Roman history, may also have been made for Marino, but form a distinct series.

Two other drawings, also from the Massimi collection (Nos. 163, 164), are closely related to the Marino drawings in theme and general style, but differ in technique and size. They must be of the same date as the others, and may also have been executed for Marino. To these fifteen possible Marino drawings Friedlaender (*Burlington*, liv, p. 254) adds No. 265, which is, however, a studio work in a totally different style and is not connected with the series.

Marino was in Paris from 1615 to 1623, during which period Poussin was also there. There is nothing to indicate the exact date at which the drawings were made, but in view of their similarity to certain designs made after Poussin went to Rome in 1624 it seems likely that they date from the later part of Marino's stay, probably from the years 1620–23.

Bellori and Félibien say that the drawings were based on Marino's poem, the *Adone*. This is, however, only true in a general sense. The themes were no doubt supplied by Marino, but they are not taken directly from his own works. The mythological subjects are mainly based on Ovid, though some, e.g. the Birth of Priapus, are not mentioned by him. The battle scenes are taken from Virgil and Livy.

The drawings were evidently not intended as preludes to paintings, but were planned to be complete in themselves. At most, Poussin may have hoped to have had them engraved. If this is the case, he probably had in mind a volume like the French translation of Ovid published in Paris in 1619 which contains copies of Tempesta's engravings, the originals of which must have been a direct source of inspiration to Poussin in this series.

154.   The Birth of Adonis.   *Pl. 22.* No. 11933.

183 mm. × 325 mm. Pen and bistre with grey wash.

Massimi 29—Literature: Bellori, *Vite*, p. 410; *F.A.Q.R.*, i, p. 273; Friedlaender, *Burlington*, liv, pp. 121, 235.

The subject is taken from Ovid, *Met.*, x, 503. The Naiads receive Adonis, born from the trunk of the tree into which his mother, Myrrha, had been transformed. The drawing is described in detail by Bellori.

155. Apollo guarding the Herds of Admetus.

Pl. 21. No. 11947.

186 mm. × 320 mm. Pen and bistre with grey wash.

Massimi 3—Literature: *F.A.Q.R.*, i, p. 268; Friedlaender, *Burlington*, liv, p. 253.

The author of the Massimi catalogue describes this as 'Mercurio in habito di Pastore'. His account is not,

however, even consistent, for after identifying the seated piper as Mercury, he states that the two kneeling figures apparently making love are Jupiter and Maia, from whose union Mercury sprang.

The subject of Europa and the herds of Agenor has also been suggested but hardly seems to fit the drawing. It seems more likely that the shepherd is Apollo and that Poussin had in mind the lines in the *Metamorphoses* (ii, 676) in which Ovid addresses him as follows: 'In those days thou wast dwelling in Elis and the Messenian fields. Thy garment was a shepherd's cloak, thy staff a stout stick from the wood, and a pipe made of seven unequal reeds was in thy hand. And while thy thoughts were all of love, and whilst thou didst discourse sweetly on the pipe, the cattle thou wast keeping strayed, it is said, all unguarded into the Pylian fields.' The object of Apollo's love is not clear. Poussin may have been combining the above passage with another from the *Heroides* of Ovid (v, 139), in which the poet describes him as courting Oenone in the guise of a shepherd.

The format and technique of the drawing indicate strongly that it belongs to the Marino series, but the line is firmer and more fluent than in any other of the set, and is closer to drawings of the 'thirties.

156. Dryope.   *Pl. 15.* No. 11941.

157 mm. × 333 mm. Pen and bistre with grey wash.

Massimi 4—Literature: *F.A.Q.R.*, i, p. 269; Friedlaender, *Burlington*, liv, p. 253.

The story of Dryope is told by Ovid (*Met.*, ix, 329). The author of the Massimi catalogue has, however, gone astray in his interpretation of the details. He describes the scene as Dryope plucking the lotus flower which is in reality the nymph Lotis transformed. Actually, however, Poussin has represented the last stage of the story, when Dryope has already been transformed into a tree for unwittingly picking the lotus flower. In her last words Dryope asked that her son should come and play near the tree, and that he should be taught that all flowers are goddesses in disguise. In the drawing we see a woman, either the nurse or Dryope's sister Iole, impressing this lesson on Dryope's child, Amphissus, who is playing by the stream with other children, some of them winged putti. Other figures look on, and on the extreme right two men talk to another man who looks over a wall. The author of the Massimi catalogue tries to explain the obscurities of the design by saying that Poussin introduced into it the story of Iolaus, told by Ovid immediately after that of Dryope (*Met.*, ix, 394); but the adventures of Iolaus do not in any way fit the drawing.

157. Orpheus in Hades.   *Pl. 17.* No. 11937.

192 mm. × 322 mm. Pen and bistre with grey wash.

Massimi 28—Literature: *F.A.Q.R.*, i, p. 273; Friedlaender, *Burlington*, liv, p. 255.

Ovid describes this scene in *Met.*, x, 11ff. Orpheus with his lyre kneels before Pluto who is accompanied by Proserpine, while Cerberus lies at his feet. Eurydice stands in an attitude of supplication before Pluto. In the left foreground is Tantalus, on the right Tityus, Sisyphus, Ixion and the Danaids, and behind them the Furies. The figure of Tityus shows the influence of Michelangelo more strongly perhaps than any other figure by Poussin, though even here the master is seen through the eyes of French Mannerists of the second school of Fontainebleau.

158. The Death of Chione. *Pl. 18.* No. 11935.

187 mm. × 317 mm. Pen and bistre with dark grey-brown wash.

Massimi 30—Literature: Chamberlaine, pl. 62; *F.A.Q.R.*, i, p. 273; Friedlaender, *Burlington*, liv, pp. 127, 255.

According to Ovid (*Met.*, xi, 321), Chione was shot through the tongue by Diana for boasting that she was more beautiful than the goddess. She is mourned over by her husband, Daedalion, and her two children, Autolycus and Philammon, the offspring of Mercury and Apollo respectively.

This rare theme was treated in a somewhat similar manner by Primaticcio.

159. Polyphemus, Acis and Galatea. *Pl. 20.* No. 11940.

186 mm. × 325 mm. Pen and grey-brown wash with traces of pencil.

Massimi 33—Literature: *F.A.Q.R.*, i, p. 274; Friedlaender, *Burlington*, liv, p. 255.

Polyphemus, after singing in vain his love for Galatea, finds her in the arms of Acis (cf. Ovid, *Met.*, xiii, 870). He is here shown just about to crush the lovers by hurling a rock at them.

This drawing is an extreme example of Poussin's use of the Mannerist device of deliberately exaggerating the difference in scale between foreground and background figures.

160. Acis transformed into a river-god.
Pl. 14. No. 11939.

189 mm. × 319 mm. Pen and bistre, with grey and dark bistre wash and traces of black chalk.

Massimi 34—Literature: *F.A.Q.R.*, i, p. 274; Friedlaender, *Burlington*, liv, p. 255.

According to the Massimi catalogue this drawing represents Byblis who, consumed by passion for her brother Caunus, was transformed into a fountain (Ovid, *Met.*, ix, 454). But the drawing does not fit the story, above all because the naked figure standing in the water is evidently a man, and not a woman.

No myth in the *Metamorphoses* suits the drawing exactly, but the one which approaches it most nearly is the end of the story of Acis (xiii, 885). When he was crushed under the rock hurled by Polyphemus, his blood flowing

from under the rock was transformed into a stream, at the command of Galatea, and the rock itself split. From this cleft sprang a reed which turned into a youth standing waist-deep in the water, his head crowned with reeds. This youth was Acis revived. This story fits with the drawing, except that Ovid refers to Acis' 'new-sprung horns' which are not apparent, and that there is no justification for the crowd of onlookers.

161. Thetis and Achilles. *Pl. 19.* No. 11934.

192 mm. × 327 mm. Pen and bistre with grey wash.

Massimi 32—Literature: *F.A.Q.R.*, i, p. 274; Friedlaender, *Burlington*, liv, p. 255.

This subject is not described by Ovid, though he refers to it in passing (*Met.*, xiii, 288). The story is, however, told by Homer (*Iliad*, xix, 1).

After the death of Patroclus, who was killed wearing the armour of Achilles, the latter was left without armour. His mother, Thetis, however, persuaded Vulcan to make him new arms, which she and her nymphs brought to Achilles.

162. The Birth of Priapus. *Pl. 16.* No. 11938.

195 mm. × 325 mm. Pen and grey-brown wash with traces of black chalk.

Massimi 14—Literature: *F.A.Q.R.*, i, p. 270; Friedlaender, *Burlington*, liv, p. 253.

The subject is not mentioned by Ovid, but is referred to by many ancient authors, e.g. by Diodorus Siculus (iv, 6). Priapus, who was the son of Venus and Bacchus, was cursed before his birth by Juno, and as a result was born with a monstrous deformity. Poussin shows Venus lying on a bed, surrounded by nymphs and Sileni. Some of the nymphs look away in horror at the child's deformity.

163. *Recto:* Mercury and Argus. *Pl. 24.* No. 11945.

272 mm. × 201 mm. Pen and dark grey wash.

Massimi 17—Literature: *F.A.Q.R.*, i, p. 271; Friedlaender, *Burlington*, liv, p. 253.

Mercury is seen in the act of killing Argus, while Io, transformed into a heifer, appears in the background (cf. Ovid, *Met.*, i, 713).

This drawing and No. 164 differ from the Marino series in format and technique. On the other hand, in theme and general style they stand very close to them, and must have been executed about the same time, namely 1620–24.

Verso: A pencil drawing of a man seen from behind. This sketch cannot be connected with any known composition, but the elegant Mannerist pose recalls paintings such as the 'Death of Germanicus'. It probably dates from about the same time as the drawing on the recto.

164. Pallas and the Muses.   *Pl. 23.* No. 11946.

307 mm. × 222 mm. Pen and dark grey wash.

Massimi 24—Literature: *F.A.Q.R.*, i, p. 272; Friedlaender, *Burlington*, liv, p. 254.

Pallas is seen alighting on Helicon as described by Ovid
(*Met.*, v, 254). A pair to No. 163.

165. The Death of Camilla.   *Pl. 27.* No. 11936.

185 mm. × 327 mm. Pen and bistre with grey wash.

Massimi 44—Literature: *F.A.Q.R.*, ii, p. 177; Friedlaender, *Burlington*, liv, p. 256.

The story is told by Virgil (*Aeneid*, xi, 799). Camilla,
daughter of Metabus, king of the Volsci, is seen dying,
struck down by the spear of Aruns, one of the companions of Aeneas.

The drawing is closely similar to the Marino series
(cf. particularly the architecture in No. 156, and the
trees and contrasts of light and shade in No. 161).

166. Battle of the Rutuli and the Trojans.   No. 11942.

190 mm. × 323 mm. Pen and bistre with grey-brown
wash.

Massimi 42—Literature: *F.A.Q.R.*, ii, p. 176; Friedlaender, *Burlington*, liv, p. 256.

According to the Massimi catalogue this drawing
shows the Trojans defending their newly founded city
against the Latins. The incident referred to is probably
the attack of Turnus and the Rutuli, described by Virgil
(*Aeneid*, ix, 1) and Livy (II, ii, 1).

This and the following drawings are similar in their
handling to the Marino mythological series, but are
more crowded in composition and more violent in movement. They show the influence of Roman reliefs and of
the engravings of the school of Giulio Romano, and are
close to two biblical battle scenes painted by Poussin just
after his arrival in Rome, and now in Leningrad and
Moscow (Grautoff, Nos. 4, 5).

167. Battle of the Romans and the Sabines.
                                     Pl. 25. No. 11943.

180 mm. × 318 mm. Pen and bistre with grey wash.

Massimi 38—Literature: *F.A.Q.R.*, ii, p. 175; Friedlaender, *Burlington*, liv, p. 256.

This appears to be the battle described by Livy (I, xi, 5)
in which the Romans were victorious owing to the aid of
Jupiter.

168. Battle of the Latins and the Romans.   No. 11944.

183 mm. × 327 mm. Pen and bistre with grey and
brown wash.

Massimi 39—Literature: *F.A.Q.R.*, ii, p. 176; Friedlaender, *Burlington*, liv, p. 256.

The Massimi catalogue describes this drawing as the
attack on the Romans by the allies of the Sabines after

the Rape of the Sabine women. This probably refers to
the battle described by Livy (I, x, 1).

B. Early Roman Drawings (1624–30).

169. The Kingdom of Flora.   *Pl. 26.* No. 11983.

213 mm. × 293 mm. Pen and bistre wash over red
chalk on rough paper.

Massimi 35—Literature: *F.A.Q.R.*, i, p. 274; Friedlaender, *Burlington*, liv, p. 255.

Study for the paintings at Dresden (Grautoff, No. 82).
The subject may have been suggested by Ovid's description of the Kingdom of Flowers in the *Fasti* (v, 183), but
Poussin has introduced details borrowed from the
Metamorphoses. The figures are usually identified as
follows: on the left Ajax falls on his sword, Clytia looks
up at the sun, Narcissus gazes at his reflection while
Echo sits by him; on the right stand Hyacinthus and
Adonis, while Crocus and Smylax lie at their feet. Flora
herself stands in the centre, and Apollo drives his chariot
across the sky. In the painting many details are altered,
but the themes and the general composition remain the
same. A finished studio drawing of the same composition
is described under No. 223.

170. 'La Tintura del Corallo.'   *Pl. 28.* No. 11984.

228 mm. × 314 mm. Pen and bistre wash over red
chalk on rough paper.

Massimi, 23—Literature: *F.A.Q.R.*, i, p. 272; Friedlaender, *Burlington*, liv, pp. 127, 254.

This drawing seems to be intended as a pendant to
No. 169.

The subject is taken from Ovid (*Met.*, iv, 740). Perseus,
after killing the sea-monster, washes the blood of the
latter from his hands. Before doing so he has laid the
head of the Medusa on the ground, and the plants
which it touches harden into coral. Hence the title which
Bellori gives to this composition: 'La Tintura del
Corallo'. Sébastien Bourdon used this drawing or No.
225 below as a basis for his painting of the same subject
in Munich.

A finished studio drawing of the same composition is
described under No. 225.

This particular episode from the story of Perseus and
Andromeda is rare in art, and it is interesting to note
that Cardinal Massimi, to whom this drawing belonged,
commissioned a painting of it from Claude, now in
Lord Leicester's Collection. (L.V. 184.)

171. Abraham driving out Hagar.   No. 11982.

185 mm. × 256 mm. Pen and bistre wash over pencil.
In lower right-hand corner the figure 4.

II, 4—Literature: *F.A.Q.R.*, iii, p. 107; Friedlaender,
Drawings, i, p. 3, B3.

Owing to its hesitant line and general feebleness this drawing was classed in the Catalogue Raisonné of Poussin's drawings as a studio work. On the other hand its similarity with certain authentic works suggests that this judgment needs revision. Many details (e.g. the head of Abraham, indication of plants in foreground) recall the 'Achelous' (No. 173); the head of Hagar has many parallels in the Marino series; the eyes of the two children and of Sarah's attendant, indicated by a single curve, recall those of certain warriors in No. 180; and details of setting in both foreground and background are closely reminiscent of No. 176. In view of these parallels the drawing should probably be regarded as a rather hesitant but genuine work of the late 'twenties.

172. The Triumph of Bacchus and Ariadne. No. 11990.

126 mm. × 425 mm. Pen and grey wash over red chalk.

Massimi 18—Literature: *F.A.Q.R.*, i, p. 271; Friedlaender, *Burlington*, liv, p. 253.

A rather weak but apparently genuine drawing with affinities to the other drawings of the late 'twenties, particularly in the schematic indication of heads. Like No. 174, however, it foreshadows the great Bacchic compositions of the middle 'thirties.

173. Achelous. No. 11986.

124 mm. × 138 mm. Pen and bistre wash over red chalk. Roughly cut round top.

Massimi 5—Literature: *F.A.Q.R.*, i, p. 269; Friedlaender, *Burlington*, liv, p. 253.

The defeat of Achelous by Hercules in their struggle for Deianira is described by Ovid (*Met.*, ix, 1). The horn which Hercules broke from the head of Achelous when the latter transformed himself into a bull during the fight became the cornucopia and was presented to Ceres. It is here seen carried by a putto.

The drawing is a fragment of a larger composition. If the river god is in fact Achelous the whole scene would probably have shown Hercules carrying off Deianira, as in No. 207. Close in style to No. 170.

174. Dance in honour of Pan. *Pl. 29.* No. 11979.

209 mm. × 328 mm. Pen and bistre wash.

Massimi 20—Literature: Chamberlaine, pl. 42; *F.A.Q.R.*, i, p. 271; Friedlaender, *Burlington*, liv, p. 254; *Seventeenth Century Art*, R.A., 1938, p. 176, No. 524.

The earliest of Poussin's many scenes illustrating dances to Pan or Bacchus. In composition it comes near to the 'Bacchanal' in the National Gallery (Grautoff, No. 83), which, however, dates from the second half of the 'thirties.

175. Mars and Venus. No. 11975.

211 mm. × 272 mm. Pen and bistre wash over black chalk.

D*

Massimi 47—Literature: *F.A.Q.R.*, i, p. 177; Friedlaender, *Burlington*, liv, p. 256; Friedlaender, *Gazette des Beaux-Arts*, 6th series, xxii, p. 24.

Engraved by Fabrizio Chiari in 1635 (Andresen, No. 349).

Study for the painting formerly at Nuneham Park, now in the Museum of Fine Arts, Boston, c. 1628–30 (Grautoff, No. 32), which, however, differs considerably from it.

This drawing is so much feebler than any others of Poussin's early sketches that in spite of its provenance from the Massimi collection and its connection with a known painting it may be a copy.

176. Nymph, Satyr and Cupid. *Pl. 30.* No. 11980.

118 mm. × 142 mm. Pen and grey-brown wash over black chalk.

Massimi 6—Literature: *F.A.Q.R.*, i, p. 269; Friedlaender, *Burlington*, liv, p. 253.

According to the Massimi catalogue this drawing represents Venus, Cupid and Pan. Poussin probably had in mind the theme of 'Amor vincit Pan' illustrated in an engraving by Agostino Carracci.

For another slightly later drawing of the same subject by Poussin cf. No. 185.

177. Satyr and Child. *Pl. 31.* No. 11981.

132 mm. × 98 mm. Pen and bistre with grey-brown wash over black chalk.

Massimi 12—Literature: *F.A.Q.R.*, i, p. 270; Friedlaender, *Burlington*, liv, p. 253.

According to the Massimi catalogue the satyr is Pan and the child Apollo, but it seems more likely that, like No. 173 above, this is a fragment of a Bacchic scene.

178. Diana hunting. *Pl. 32.* No. 11985.

151 mm. × 239 mm. Pen and bistre on pale blue paper.

Massimi 16—Literature: *F.A.Q.R.*, i, p. 270; Friedlaender, *Burlington*, liv, p. 253.

A fragment. Unusual in being in pen only, without wash.

179. Le Fanciulle Rusticane. *Pl. 33.* No. 036.

182 mm. × 247 mm. Pen and bistre on dark blue paper.
Massimi 68—Literature: *F.A.Q.R.*, ii, p. 180.

Friedlaender (*Burlington*, liv, p. 257) wrongly identifies No. 68 of the Massimi catalogue as drawing No. 272. The description, however, specifically mentions 'un bambino che dorme' at the feet of one of the girls, and this feature is absent from No. 272. Moreover the dimensions and technique as given by Woodward when the Massimi volume was still intact fit this drawing and not No. 272.

The drawing is unique in Poussin's *œuvre* in that it represents a genre scene, and it is very unusual in style. The quality of its line, however, and the use of hatching are exactly like No. 178; and the drawing of the faces, with simplified profile and eyes indicated by a single line, is close to No. 169. These parallels, combined with the provenance of the drawing from the Massimi collection, leave very little doubt that the drawing is in fact from Poussin's own hand.

180. *Recto:* Battle of the Israelites and the Midianites.
Pl. 34. No. 11884.

164 mm. × 281 mm. Pen and bistre wash over black chalk.

II, 13—Literature: *F.A.Q.R.*, iii, p. 110.

The subject is wrongly described in *F.A.Q.R.* as 'The Sabine Women'. Actually it is taken from Numbers xxxi, 1–12, and represents the victory of the Israelites over the Midianites described there. In general the drawing is like the Roman battle scenes, Nos. 165–168 and the women on the left recall the nymphs in No. 174.

Verso: The Golden Calf.

Faint black chalk.

Literature: Friedlaender, *Drawings*, i, p. 12, No. 22.

A study for the painting of 1629 (cf. *Burlington*, xxxv, 1919, p. 90). Both drawings, recto and verso, can be dated to about this year.

181. *Recto:* The Victory of Godfrey de Bouillon.
Pl. 35. No. 11882.

196 mm. × 563 mm. Pen and bistre wash.

Massimi 73—Literature: *F.A.Q.R.*, ii, p. 181; Friedlaender, *Burlington*, liv, p. 258.

As the Massimi catalogue indicates, the theme is the last battle in the *Gerusalemme Liberata* (Canto xx) in which Godfrey and the Christians defeated the King of Egypt. In style this drawing is very close to the 'Battle of the Israelites and the Midianites' (cf. above No. 180), and indeed one group towards the left of the composition repeats exactly one in the latter. It is, however, a little more elegant, and is therefore probably slightly later, 1628–30.

Verso: A faint sketch of the same subject.

Black chalk.

182. Study for the Triumph of David.   No. 037.

108 mm. × 95 mm. Pen and bistre wash over black chalk. Roughly cut round top.

Massimi 50—Literature: *F.A.Q.R.*, ii, p. 178; Friedlaender, *Drawings*, i, p. 14, No. 30.

The Massimi catalogue suggests that this drawing represents the women of Israel offering gifts to Moses. In fact, however, it is a study for a group in the 'Triumph of David' at Dulwich, painted about 1628. It is probably a fragment of a larger drawing. Another study for the

same group is at Chantilly (cf. Friedlaender, *Drawings*, i, p. 14, No. 29).

183. The Ascension.   *Pl. 38.* No. 0749.

145 mm. × 265 mm. Red chalk.

Massimi 61—Literature: *F.A.Q.R.*, ii, p. 180.

A fragment, showing only the Apostles, the top with the figure of Christ being lost.

This drawing is unusual for Poussin in both style and technique, and is difficult to place in his *œuvre*. If it had not belonged to the Massimi volume it might not have been regarded as being by him. On the other hand it is clearly not a copy or studio work, and must be considered genuine. It is close to certain studies by Domenichino (e.g. at Windsor Nos. 789, 1010), which, however, are always more precise in detail. The simple outlines of heads in the present drawing are related to Poussin's pen drawings of the late 'twenties (cf. No. 181), which was also the moment when Poussin first came under the influence of Domenichino. The drawing therefore probably dates from that period. It is possible that other drawings of this period, such as No. 173, may have had something of this character in handling when the red chalk under-drawing only was finished and the thick pen strokes were not yet added.

183a. See page 81.

C. Drawings executed in Rome in the years 1630–1641, before the Paris journey.

184. *Recto:* God the Father supported by cherubs.
Pl. 36. No. 0750.

110 mm. × 184 mm. Pen and bistre.

Massimi 2—Literature: *F.A.Q.R.*, i, p. 268.

This drawing is a fragment, and may, as the author of the Massimi catalogue suggests, be a part of a 'Creation of the World'. It is more likely, however, to belong to a 'Sacrifice of Noah' or 'Moses and the Burning Bush'. The line still has some of the coarseness of the early sketches, but it is somewhat thinner, which suggests a date about 1630. Another drawing of the same subject, also rather weak, is at Chantilly (cf. Friedlaender, *Drawings*, i, p. 3, No. 1).

Verso: Faint sketch of a seated figure.

Red chalk.

185. *Recto:* Nymph, Satyr and Cupid.   No. 11915.

128 mm. × 100 mm. Pen and bistre wash over black chalk. Patched in one place.

Massimi 11—Literature: *F.A.Q.R.*, i, p. 270; Friedlaender, *Burlington*, liv, p. 253.

The theme is the same as in No. 176. About 1630.

Verso: Studies of a centaur.

Pen and bistre.

Probably connected with a composition of the Battle of Hercules and the Centaurs.

186. Nymph and Satyr. No. 11987.

125 mm. × 264 mm. Pen and bistre wash. Cut off and patched at the top, probably with another part of the same drawing.

Massimi 13—Literature: *F.A.Q.R.*, i, p. 270; Friedlaender, *Burlington*, liv, p. 253.

According to the Massimi catalogue the principal figure is Venus and not a nymph. The theme, which is familiar in ancient reliefs, occurs in two paintings connected with Poussin, a very damaged canvas of doubtful authenticity in the National Gallery (Grautoff, No. 24), and a genuine work in a Swiss private collection (cf. *Gazette des Beaux-Arts*, 1932, i, p. 326). The drawing varies in several particulars from both paintings.

187. Three Nymphs. *Pl. 39.* No. 11914.

131 mm. × 146 mm. Pen and bistre over black chalk.

Massimi 10—Literature: *F.A.Q.R.*, i, p. 269; Friedlaender, *Burlington*, liv, pp. 127, 253.

Described in the Massimi catalogue as 'Tyro and the Nymphs'. The story of Tyro is told by Homer (*Od.* xi, 235). She was ravished by Neptune, who assumed the form of her lover, the river-god Enipeus. If it represents this theme, the drawing is singularly inexpressive, since both nymphs and river-god—visible on the right, but partly cut off by the edge of the drawing—are purely passive. It is more likely to be a fragment of a larger mythological subject of which the central figures are lost. In this case the figures are simply nymphs and a river-god. About 1633–35.

188. A Nymph. No. 11922.

154 mm. × 109 mm. Pen and bistre. Inscribed on the verso: *Molto mag.^e*, not in Poussin's hand.

A nymph sitting under a tree on which hang a bow, quiver and cloak. Perhaps a study for a composition of Diana hunting. About 1633–35.

189. *Recto:* The Saving of Pyrrhus. *Pl. 40.* No. 11909.

210 mm. × 346 mm. Pen and dark bistre wash over red chalk.

Massimi 41—Literature: *F.A.Q.R.*, ii, p. 176; Friedlaender, *Burlington*, liv, pp. 128, 256.

Plutarch (*Life of Pyrrhus*, ii) tells the story as follows: Pyrrhus was the son of Aeacides, King of Epirus, who was driven out of his kingdom by the Molossians. His friends saved the child Pyrrhus and carried him to Megara, where they informed the inhabitants of their distress by hurling across the river a spear and a stone to which messages were attached. The Megarans then sent over a boat to fetch them.

Preliminary sketch for the painting in the Louvre (Grautoff, No. 57), executed about 1635. The two men hurling the spear and the stone are closely connected with two of the studies which Poussin made for Leonardo's treatise (cf. below Nos. 230, 240).

Verso: Sketch for the right half of the same composition. Pen and bistre.

190. The Schoolmaster of Falerii. *Pl. 37.* No. 11913.

178 mm. × 181 mm. Pen and dark bistre wash; torn.

Massimi 40—Literature: *F.A.Q.R.*, ii. p. 176; Friedlaender, *Burlington*, liv, pp. 128, 256.

According to Valerius Maximus (VI, 5, 1), Furius Camillus was besieging Falerii when a Faeliscian schoolmaster led his pupils out and offered them as hostages to the Roman general. As a reward for his treachery, the general handed him over to be beaten by his own pupils.

According to Félibien (*Entretiens*, iv, p. 25) Poussin painted two versions of this subject: one about 1635, later with Passart, and recently in the collection of Prince Paul of Jugoslavia (cf. *Gazette des Beaux-Arts*, 1931, ii, p. 52); and the second larger version for La Vrillière in 1637, now in the Louvre (Grautoff, No. 69). This drawing is a study for the earlier painting, but its action is more concentrated. Executed about 1635. A drawing for yet another version of this subject is in the British Museum (1895–9–22).

191. The Rape of the Sabines. *Pl. 45.* No. 11903.

115 mm. × 196 mm. Pen and bistre wash over black chalk.

Massimi 37—Literature: *F.A.Q.R.*, ii, p. 175; Borenius, 'An Exhibition of Poussin and Claude Drawings', *Old Master Drawings*, iii, 1928, p. 18; Friedlaender, *Burlington*, liv, p. 255.

Poussin executed two paintings of this subject: one for Cardinal Omodei, described by Bellori (*Vite*, p. 449), is now in the Louvre (Grautoff, No. 70). The other mentioned by Félibien was in the Cook Collection (Grautoff, No. 71). The Louvre version dates from about 1633–35, the Cook painting from about 1637. This drawing is a study for the Cook version, but differs from it in many details. Probably executed 1635–37.

Other drawings connected with the same composition are at Windsor (see next number), Uffizi (9001), and Chatsworth (861). A wholly different treatment of the same theme appears in two drawings at Chantilly and Besançon.

192. The Rape of the Sabines. *Pl. 44.* No. 11904.

110 mm. × 80 mm. Pen and bistre wash with black chalk.

Literature: *F.A.Q.R.*, ii, p. 175; Borenius, 'An Exhibition of Poussin and Claude Drawings', *Old Master*

Drawings, iii, 1928, p. 18; Friedlaender, *Burlington*, liv, pp. 127, 255.

This drawing is not directly connected with either painting. In theme and by its vertical movement it is closer to the Louvre version, but it is so similar to the last drawing that they cannot be far separated in date. 1635–37.

Not from the Massimi volume as suggested tentatively by Friedlaender (cf. *F.A.Q.R.*, ii, p. 175).

Fig. 2. NICOLAS POUSSIN: Rinaldo and Armida. Catalogue No. 201

193. *Recto:* The Death of Virginia.   *Pl. 41.* No. 11888.

174 mm. × 230 mm. Pen and bistre wash.

II, 14—Literature: *F.A.Q.R.*, iii, p. 110.

Valerius Maximus (VI, 1, 2) tells the story of Virginia who was killed by her father to save her honour, which was threatened by the decemvir, Appius Claudius. The group with the figure of the dying Virginia appears again in the drawing of the 'Finding of Queen Zenobia' (cf. No. 216). About 1635.

Verso: Bacchus and Ariadne.

Pen and bistre.

A sketch for the next drawing.

194. Bacchus and Ariadne.   *Pl. 42.* No. 11911.

156 mm. × 250 mm. Pen and bistre wash on pinkish paper.

II, 17—Literature: Borenius, 'An Exhibition of Poussin and Claude Drawings', *Old Master Drawings*, iii, 1928, pp. 17, 18.

Bacchus, accompanied by attendants, greets Ariadne who is in tears at finding herself deserted by Theseus.

The sketch on the verso of No. 193 shows a rather more elaborate version of the scene. In handling both drawings are very close to the 'Death of Virginia' (No. 193), and in general composition they recall the Bacchanals of the middle 'thirties. The drawings were therefore probably executed about 1635.

195. St. Mary of Egypt and St. Zosimus.
                                  Pl. 43. No. 11925.

225 mm. × 310 mm. Pen and bistre wash.

Massimi 66—Literature: *F.A.Q.R.*, ii, p. 180; Borenius, 'An Exhibition of Poussin and Claude Drawings', *Old Master Drawings*, iii, 1928, p. 18 and pl. 19; Friedlaender, *Burlington*, liv, p. 257; *French Art*, R.A., 1932, p. 139, No. 624; *Seventeenth Century Art*, R.A., 1938, p. 171, No. 503.

St. Mary of Egypt is here seen receiving the Sacrament from St. Zosimus by the Jordan, after spending forty-seven years in the desert. This drawing is of great importance historically, since it is probably the earliest surviving example of Poussin's experiments in the field of landscape. The brilliant use of different tones of bistre wash and the drawing of the figures both point to a date about 1635, which is thirteen years earlier than Poussin's first recorded landscape paintings.

196. The Agony in the Garden.   *Pl. 46.* No. 11997.

Upper part 175 mm. × 245 mm. Lower part 105 mm. × 240 mm. Pen and bistre wash on pale blue paper.

Lower part: Massimi 59. Upper part: II, 1b—Literature: *F.A.Q.R.*, ii, p. 179, and iii, p. 106; Friedlaender, *Burlington*, liv, p. 257; Friedlaender, *Drawings*, i, p. 33, No. 64; *Seventeenth Century Art*, R.A., 1938, p. 176, No. 526.

This drawing may possibly be connected with the painting of the same subject mentioned by Sandrart as being in the possession of Cassiano del Pozzo (*Teutsche Akademie*, ed. Peltzer, 1925, p. 258). The lighting is unusually dramatic for Poussin. Probably executed about the middle of the 'thirties.

197. Two ancient Statues.   No. 11916.

168 mm. × 119 mm. Pen and bistre.

Massimi 46—Literature: *F.A.Q.R.*, ii, p. 177; Friedlaender, *Burlington*, liv, p. 256.

Cassiano del Pozzo employed a circle of artists, among whom was Poussin, to make drawings after the remains of ancient statues, paintings and architecture. A large part of the collection made in this way is preserved in a series of volumes which came to the Royal Library from the Albani collection. Other drawings of the same kind exist elsewhere, many of them attributed to Poussin, but few of them actually from his hand. The present drawing, however, which formed part of the Massimi volume, is unquestionably genuine. The quality of line places the drawing close to the 'Death of Virginia' (No. 193), and the heads, only indicated in outline, recall the Madonna and Child on the verso of No. 214. About 1635.

198. Bacchanal before a Temple.   *Pl. 49.* No. 11910.

210 mm. × 316 mm. Pen and bistre wash; torn.

Massimi 19—Literature: *F.A.Q.R.*, i, p. 271; Friedlaender, *Burlington*, liv, pp. 127, 253.

This drawing is described in the Massimi catalogue as 'Li Misteri di Priapo', but it seems rather to represent a strictly Bacchic scene. A study for a painting now lost, but known in copies, one of which is in the possession of Capt. R. G. Briscoe, M.P. (cf. B.F.A.C. Winter Exhib., 1930–31, No. 2), and from an engraving by Mariette dated 1688 (Andresen, No. 367). About 1635.

Another drawing for the same composition is at Chantilly (cf. Malo, Cent deux dessins de N. Poussin, No. 39).

199. *Recto:* The Indian Triumph of Bacchus.
Pl. 48. No. 11905.

191 mm. × 291 mm. Pen and bistre.

Massimi 21—Literature: F.A.Q.R., i, p. 271; Friedlaender, *Burlington*, liv, pp. 127, 254; *Seventeenth Century Art*, R.A., 1938, p. 173, No. 515.

The drawing shows Bacchus returning from India, seated in a chariot drawn by leopards, and accompanied by elephants, giraffes and camels.

On the right are two detailed studies for the chariot.

The drawing is not directly connected with any known painting, but belongs in character to the series of big Bacchanal subjects designed about 1635–39.

Verso: Dance in honour of Pan.
Pl. 47.

Pen and bistre.

Two vigorous sketches for the composition carried out as one of the Bacchanals for Richelieu about 1635–37. The painting is in the Morrison collection (Grautoff, No. 85). Other original drawings connected with this design are at Windsor (Nos. 219 verso, 200), and at Bayonne (1669, 1671, 1672).

200. Bacchanal.
No. 11995.

229 mm. × 335 mm. Pen and bistre wash.

Massimi 22—Literature: F.A.Q.R., i, p. 271; Friedlaender, *Burlington*, liv, p. 254.

An elaborate drawing for the Bacchanal in the Morrison collection, cf. Nos. 199 verso and 219 verso.

This drawing is unusual in style and in certain ways looks like a studio work. But it is more vigorous than any other studio products, and probably represents Poussin's manner when he was working up a finished composition.

201. Study for 'Rinaldo and Armida'. *Fig. 2.* No. 11923.

102 mm. × 148 mm. Pen and bistre.

Massimi 9—Literature: F.A.Q.R., i, p. 269; Friedlaender, *Burlington*, liv, p. 253.

This drawing is described in the Massimi catalogue as 'Galathea alle riva del fiume Aci', but it is in fact a study for the right-hand group in the composition of Armida carrying off Rinaldo, executed for Stella about 1637 (cf. *Correspondance*, p. 3; Félibien, *Entretiens*, iv, p. 25). The original is now lost, but copies are known,

one in Berlin (Friedlaender, *Nicolas Poussin*, 1914, p. 180), and one having appeared at Robinson and Fisher (23.3.1939, lot 32). The scene is from Canto XIV of the *Gerusalemme Liberata*.

Fig. 3. NICOLAS POUSSIN: Seated Woman.
Catalogue No. 202

The group shown here is not exactly reproduced in the painting, but appears in a study for it, Louvre 756. Another drawing for the same composition is also in the Louvre (32435), and a finished studio drawing is at Windsor (see No. 226).

202. Sketch of a Seated Woman. *Fig. 3.* No. 11924.

114 mm. × 77 mm. Pen and bistre.

Similar in style to Nos. 201, 203. About 1637.

203. *Recto:* Charity.
No. 11921.

119 mm. × 150 mm. Pen and bistre over black chalk.

Massimi 67—Literature: F.A.Q.R., ii, p. 180; Friedlaender, *Burlington*, liv, pp. 127, 257.

A woman gives food to a child, while two other children cling to her. The style is like that of No. 219 verso. The figure of the seated woman was used as the basis for the engraving of 'Industria' in the 1640 edition of Francesco Barberino's *Documenti d'Amore* (p. 90), which bears the inscription: C. Massimi fec. G. F. Greuter int.

For the shares of Poussin and Camillo Massimi in the plates to this volume see below No. 212. The present drawing appears to date from about 1637–39.

Verso: Truth revealed by Time.

Pen and bistre.

Study for a lost painting described by Bellori (*Vite*, p. 448) known from a copy in a private collection, and from engravings by Giovanni Folo and J. Dughet (Andresen, Nos. 407, 408).

The manner of drawing is close to No. 201. 1637–39.

204. Marriage. *Pl. 51.* No. 11894.

195 mm. × 282 mm. Pen and bistre wash on buff paper.

Massimi 51—Literature: *F.A.Q.R.*, ii, p. 178; Friedlaender, *Burlington*, liv, p. 256; Friedlaender, *Drawings*, i, p. 44, No. 90.

Described in the Massini catalogue as 'Sposalitio di Maria'. This is correct, but the particular subject, the marriage of Joseph and Mary, is taken as the symbol of the Sacrament of marriage in general. For this drawing is a sketch for the painting representing 'Marriage' in the first series of the Seven Sacraments, painted for Cassiano del Pozzo about 1637–40, now at Belvoir Castle.

205. *Recto:* Confirmation. *Pl. 52.* No. 11896.

137 mm. × 208 mm. Pen and bistre wash over black chalk.

II, 8—Literature: *F.A.Q.R.*, iii, p. 109; Friedlaender, *Drawings*, i, p. 43, No. 85.

A study for the painting belonging to the first series of Sacraments, executed in the later 'thirties for Cassiano del Pozzo (Grautoff, No. 92).

Verso: Holy Family.

117 mm. × 134 mm. Pen and bistre. Cut off at the top.

Literature: Friedlaender, *Drawings*, i, p. 24, No. 40.

The group of Madonna and Child is close to the Roccatagliata Madonna, but the style of drawing suggests a date a year or two earlier, about 1638. This is confirmed by the drawing on the recto, and by the close connection with No. 208.

206. *Recto:* The Death of Cato the Younger. No. 11919.

96 mm. × 149 mm. Pen and bistre with traces of pencil.

Massimi 45—Literature: *F.A.Q.R.*, ii, p. 177; Friedlaender, *Burlington*, liv, p. 256.

The story is told by Plutarch (*Life of Cato the Younger*, lviii).

Cato runs himself through with a sword. Beside him is the copy of the Phaedo which he has been reading.

The style recalls drawings such as No. 203 recto. Probably about 1637–39.

Verso: Sketch of a woman in ancient costume.

Pen and bistre. Part of another sketch in black chalk.

About 1637–39.

207. *Recto:* Hercules and Deianira. *Pl. 50.* No. 11912.

220 mm. × 318 mm. Pen and bistre.

Massimi 27—Literature: *F.A.Q.R.*, i, p. 273; Friedlaender, *Burlington*, liv., pp. 127, 255.

The scene is described by Ovid (*Met.*, ix, 1). On the left Hercules, heralded by Cupid, carries off Deianira whom he has just won in combat with Achelous. The latter lies wounded beside him, while a nymph tends his head. Two putti carry the lion's skin behind the hero. On the right a nymph presents to Ceres the horn of Achelous, now become the Cornucopia, and behind her Aeneus, father of Deianira, is seen walking away. Probably a study for the painting for Chantelou, executed about 1637–39 (Félibien, *Entretiens*, iv, p. 26).

The drawing has been divided down the middle, as if Poussin intended to make two compositions of it. Other drawings are known connected with the left-hand half, which is also engraved, with considerable variations, by Audran (Andresen, No. 398).

The landscape setting recalls the outdoor scenes in the first series of Sacraments. Probably about 1637–39.

Verso: Two studies of the Holy Family.

Black chalk.

Literature: Friedlaender, *Drawings*, i, p. 24, No. 42.

Not directly connected with any known painting. But similar to the group of Madonna drawings of the late 'thirties, from which period it must also date.

208. Holy Family. No. 11917.

140 mm. × 101 mm. Pen and bistre wash.

Massimi 53—Literature: *F.A.Q.R.*, ii, p. 178; Friedlaender, *Burlington*, liv, p. 256; Friedlaender, *Drawings*, i, p. 24, No. 41.

Closely related to the Roccatagliata Madonna, painted in 1641–42, but probably a year or two earlier. On the verso is a fragment of a draft of a letter which, as has been shown by Salomon (*Journal of the Warburg Institute*, i, p. 82), must have been written at the end of 1638. Since the paper was evidently cut when the drawing was made, the drawing must be later than the draft, and therefore probably dates from 1639–40. For the full text of the letter, cf. Salomon's article.

209. *Recto:* Moses and the Daughters of Jethro.

Pl. 53. No. 11890.

145 mm. × 212 mm. Pen and bistre wash.

Massimi 48—Literature: *F.A.Q.R.*, ii, p. 177; Fried-laender, *Zeitschrift für bildende Kunst*, N.F. xxv, 1914, p. 318; Friedlaender, *Burlington*, liv, p. 256; Friedlaender, *Drawings*, i, p. 9, No. 11.

Preliminary drawing for the group of the daughters of Jethro which appears in the finished studio sketch, No. 210.

No painting is known of this composition. The style suggests the late 'thirties rather than the 'forties as suggested in Friedlaender, *Drawings*, **i**, p. 9, and should be compared with No. 205.

Verso: Sketch of the same group.

Pen and bistre.

Literature: Friedlaender, *Drawings*, i, p. 9, No. 12.

210. *Recto:* Moses and the Daughters of Jethro.

No. 11889.

192 mm. × 317 mm. Pen and bistre wash.

II, 2—Literature: *F.A.Q.R.*, iii, p. 106; Friedlaender, *Drawings*, i, p. 8, A3.

A finished sketch of the whole composition of which No. 209 forms a part. Probably studio work. A similar studio sketch for the same composition is in a private collection (cf. Friedlaender, *Drawings*, i, p. 8, No. 10).

Verso: The Combat of the Horatii and the Curiatii.

Pen and bistre wash.

The inscription, *rahuel di Madiani*, in Poussin's hand refers to the drawing on the recto. No painting of the Horatii by Poussin is known, but the semicircle drawn round this composition suggests that it may have been a sketch for a lunette. Like the drawing on the recto, this dates from the late 'thirties.

211. *Recto:* Scipio Africanus and the Pirates.

Pl. 54. No. 11886.

212 mm. × 280 mm. Pen and bistre wash.

Massimi 43—Literature: *F.A.Q.R.*, ii, p. 176; Fried-laender, *Burlington*, liv, p. 256.

Wrongly described in *F.A.Q.R.* as 'Germanicus pardoning the mutinous soldiers'. Valerius Maximus (ii, 102) gives the story of Scipio Africanus. When he had retired to his villa at Linternus, certain pirates landed, with the intention apparently of attacking the villa. When they saw Scipio's preparations for defence they threw away their arms and revealed their real intention, which was to pay homage to the general.

We know from a letter written by Poussin in Paris (*Correspondance*, p. 165) that in June 1642 he was planning a finished drawing for Cardinal Barberini on a subject connected with Scipio. He regretted, moreover, that he had left his original sketches in Rome. In July the new drawing seems to be finished (*Correspondance*, p. 169). It seems likely that the present drawing and the sketches on the verso are those left behind in Rome by Poussin,

whereas the drawing executed in Paris in 1642 is in all probability the studio piece described below under No. 251. Another preliminary drawing is in the Ecole des Beaux-Arts. This and the present drawing were probably both executed in 1639–40, just before Poussin left for Paris.

Verso: Sketches for the same subject.

Pen and bistre.

212. Cupid on horseback.　　　*Fig. 4a.* No. 11967.

154 mm. × 146 mm. Pen and bistre wash.

Massimi 7—Literature: *F.A.Q.R.*, i, p. 269; Friedlaender, *Burlington*, liv, p. 253.

212a. Cupid on horseback.　　　*Fig. 4b.* No. 11968.

118 mm. × 116 mm. Pen and bistre wash over black chalk.

Massimi 8—Literature: *F.A.Q.R.*, i, p. 269; Friedlaender, *Burlington*, liv, p. 253.

The Massimi catalogue tells us that this emblem was the creation of the 'Sublime Ingegno del Cardinale Camillo Massimo', and that it illustrates the universal power of love as described by Petrarch. Dr. Saxl, however, discovered that although images of this kind do occur in illustrations to Petrarch (cf. E. Panofsky, *Studies in Iconology*, 1939, p. 116 and Fig. 89), the present drawings are exact renderings of a passage in the *Documenti d'Amore* of the fourteenth-century poet, Francesco Barberino, and are based on an illustration in the fourteenth-century manuscript of the poem now in the Vatican (cod. Vat. Barb. xlvi, 18, now 4076), reproduced by Panofsky (cf. Fig. 4c).

The problem of the drawings is, however, more curious than this, for they agree almost exactly with the upper part of an engraving in the edition of the poem published in Rome in 1640 under the auspices of the Barberini family (Fig. 4d). The engraving itself bears the inscription: *C. Massimi fece. G. F. Greuter int.* There can be no question of the Windsor drawings being by Massimi himself, who, though he seems to have tried his hand at composition, was certainly not a professional artist. The part played by his 'sublime ingegno' cannot, therefore, have been very great, and we can only imagine that he gave general indications to Poussin for the remodelling of the image as shown in the manuscript, so that it should accord with classical taste of the seventeenth century. We do not, of course, know how far he may have contributed to the detail of the lower part of the composition, though this again is based on the manuscript illustration.

The two drawings differ from one another in detail, and there is reason to suppose that No. 212a was the one actually used for the engraving. It is in the opposite sense to the engraving, and is closer to it than No. 212 in certain details, e.g. the proportion of the figure, and

Fig. 4a. NICOLAS POUSSIN: Cupid on horseback.
Catalogue No. 212

Fig. 4b. NICOLAS POUSSIN (Studio?): Cupid on
horseback. Catalogue No. 212a

Fig. 4c. Illustration to Francesco Barberino's *Documenti
d'Amore*. Fourteenth-century manuscript

Fig. 4d. Illustration to Francesco Barberino's
Documenti d'Amore. Edition of 1640

the spray of roses running up from beside the foot of the Cupid. Both drawings are somewhat mechanical, but No. 212 is the more lively. It is therefore probable that No. 212 is Poussin's first sketch, and that No. 212a is the second version, perhaps by a competent pupil.

These drawings, which cannot have been executed after 1640, provide the earliest evidence of contact between Poussin and Camillo Massimi. The latter was only born in 1620, and it has therefore been generally assumed that he cannot have become a patron of the artist till the later 'forties. It is now, however, certain that they must have been in touch before Poussin's visit to Paris.

For another drawing by Poussin used by Massimi as the basis for an engraving to the *Documenti d'Amore* see No. 203.

D. Drawings dating from 1641 onwards. (During and after the visit to Paris.)

213. Holy Family.   *Pl. 55.* No. 11988.

213 mm. × 164 mm. Pen and bistre wash over black chalk on pale blue paper. Squared.

Massimi 54—Literature: *F.A.Q.R.*, ii, p. 179; T. Muchall-Viebrook, 'Ueber eine Zeichnung von Nicolas Poussin', *Münchner Jahrbuch*, N.F., ii, 1925, p. 102; Borenius, 'An Exhibition of Poussin and Claude Drawings', *Old Master Drawings*, iii, 1928, p. 18; Friedlaender, *Burlington*, liv, pp. 127, 257; Friedlaender, *Drawings*, i, p. 24, No. 43; *Seventeenth Century Art*, R.A., 1938, p. 174, No. 518.

This drawing is almost identical in composition with a painting known in several versions (Chantilly, National Gallery, Pavlovsk) which appears to be by Le Sueur. It seems likely, therefore, that Le Sueur was in contact with Poussin during the latter's visit to Paris in 1640–42, and that he saw and copied this or a very similar drawing at that time. We have already seen another instance of a painter turning a drawing of Poussin's to his own uses in the 'Perseus and Andromeda', adapted by Bourdon (cf. No. 170). The style of the drawing confirms the date 1641–42.

214. *Recto:* Hercules and Theseus fighting the Amazons.   *Pl. 56.* No. 11920.

132 mm. × 136 mm. The drawing itself circular. Pen and bistre wash over black chalk. Lower right-hand corner the figure 29.

II, 32a.

The number 29 on the drawing suggests that it is one of a considerable series of designs, probably intended as decoration. This indication, coupled with the subject, is strong evidence that the drawing is a design connected with the series for the decoration of the Long Gallery in the Louvre of which Hercules was to have been the hero. An earlier stage in these designs is seen in a sheet

of sketches in Bayonne (cf. *Les Dessins de la Collection Léon Bonnat au Musée de Bayonne*, 1925, pl. 39). This contains six very rough sketches of compositions in round and oblong panels, with numbers and notes on their subjects in Poussin's hand. The Windsor drawing appears to represent the next stage in the development, that is to say Poussin's fair copy of the design in more elaborate form, which in its turn would have been the basis of the finished studio drawings ready for execution in full scale of which a large number for the Long Gallery are known (cf. below Nos. 252–256).

The date of the present drawing, during the visit to Paris 1640–42, is confirmed by the sketch on the verso.

Verso: Rough sketch of the Madonna and Child.

Pen and bistre.

Literature: Friedlaender, *Drawings*, i, p. 25, No. 44.

This sketch is connected with the composition shown in the last drawing, No. 213, which was also executed during the visit to Paris.

215. *Recto:* Confirmation.   *Pl. 59.* No. 11897.

182 mm. × 256 mm. Pen and light bistre wash.

II, 7—Literature: *F.A.Q.R.*, iii, p. 108; Friedlaender, *Drawings*, i, p. 43, No. 86.

Study for the painting belonging to the second series of Sacraments, executed for Chantelou in 1644–45. Other drawings for the same composition are No. 261 below, and Louvre 994, 995, 996.

Verso: Head of a woman.

Pen and bistre.

Not connected with any known painting. About the same date as the drawing on the recto.

216. The Finding of Queen Zenobia.   *Pl. 58.* No. 11895.

154 mm. × 200 mm. Pen and bistre wash. Inscribed: *Zenobia, artaxata, araxo.*

The story of Zenobia, wife of Rhadamistus, King of Armenia, is told by Tacitus (*Ann.* xii, 51). She escaped from Artaxata with her husband after an insurrection, but, being seized during her flight with the pangs of childbirth, she begged her husband to kill her, so that she might escape her enemies. Rhadamistus stabbed her and threw her body into the Araxes, from which it was taken by shepherds, who found that the queen was still alive. The drawing represents the moment when she is being taken from the water.

The attitude of the queen is almost exactly that of Virginia in the 'Death of Virginia' (No. 193), and the use of line and wash recall the 'Confirmation' (No. 215 recto). The present drawing must therefore date from the late 'thirties or early 'forties. Other drawings illustrating the same scene are at Chantilly and in the Hermitage.

217. *Recto:* Medea killing her children. *Pl. 60.* No. 11892.

161 mm. × 167 mm. Pen and bistre.

Massimi 26—Literature: *F.A.Q.R.*, i, p. 272; Friedlaender, *Burlington*, liv, pp. 127, 254.

Medea stabs her children to avenge herself for the unfaithfulness of Jason (cf. Ovid, *Met.*, vii, 394).

A vigorous sketch with the violent expressiveness of Poussin's drawings in the late 'forties. The size and description given in *F.A.Q.R.*, show that this was the drawing in the Massimi volume, although the description in the manuscript catalogue mentions the motive of the statue of Minerva hiding her face, which only occurs in the more elaborate studio version described below (cf. No. 264). The author of the catalogue seems to have been misled by his habit of following Bellori who describes the other drawing of the subject.

Verso: Fragment of a sketch of the Holy Family.

Pen and bistre.

Literature: Friedlaender, *Burlington*, liv, p. 254; Friedlaender, *Drawings*, i, p. 29, No. 56.

Half the verso is filled with addition and subtraction sums, apparently in Poussin's hand. Dates from the late 'forties.

218. *Recto:* Moses striking the Rock. *Pl. 63.* No. 11887.

143 mm. × 364 mm. Pen and bistre wash. Lightly squared.

II, 3—Literature: *F.A.Q.R.*, iii, p. 107; Borenius, 'An Exhibition of Poussin and Claude Drawings', *Old Master Drawings*, iii, 1928, p. 18; Friedlaender, *Drawings*, i, p. 14, No. 28.

The composition is in some respects connected with the painting of the same subject at Bridgewater House, painted before 1637 for Gillier (Grautoff, No. 91). But it is much more classical in disposition and construction, and must certainly be later. Probably executed towards the end of the 'forties.

Verso: St. Matthew and the angel.

172 mm. × 117 mm. Pen.

Literature: Friedlaender, *Drawings*, i, p. 38, B18.

This drawing is lively in manner, but unusually fluent for Poussin. In Friedlaender, *Drawings*, it was published as by an imitator, but it may really be an unusual original Poussin.

219. *Recto:* Christ healing the Blind Man.   No. 11902.

142 mm. × 208 mm. Pen and bistre.

II, 8b—Literature: *F.A.Q.R.*, iii, p. 109; Friedlaender, *Drawings*, i, p. 32, No. 62.

Sketch for the painting in the Louvre executed in 1650. Another original drawing for the same composition is at Bayonne, and studio sketches for groups of disciples in it are at Windsor (cf. below Nos. 266, 267).

The sketches on the verso show that Poussin cut down an earlier sheet of drawings to make this composition. This was a usual practice with him, but in this case the difference in date between the recto and verso is unusually great, more than a decade.

Verso: Sketches for the 'Dance in honour of Pan'.

Pen and bistre. Part of another sketch in black chalk.

The sheet contains three studies. The central and right-hand groups are connected with the Morrison Bacchanal (Grautoff, No. 85), cf. No. 199 above. The middle sketch is a study for the Bacchante decorating a herm, a motive which appears also in No. 200 verso, and in the painting. On the right a Bacchante is seen leading a goat. This motive does not appear in the painting, but is to be seen in other drawings connected with it, such as Bayonne 1671, 1672. On the left is a sketch of a mourning woman, probably a study for the figure on the extreme left in the 'Extreme Unction' from the first series of Sacraments, painted in the late 'thirties.

220. The Sacrifice of Polyxena.   *Pl. 64.* No. 11906.

175 mm. × 351 mm. Pen and pale bistre wash over red chalk on rough buff paper.

Massimi 31—Literature: *F.A.Q.R.*, i, p. 274; Friedlaender, *Burlington*, liv, p. 255.

When the Greeks had left Troy, the ghost of Achilles appeared to Agamemnon and demanded that Polyxena, daughter of Priam, should be sacrificed at his tomb. His command was carried out (Ovid., *Met.*, xiii, 439).

This drawing is an impressive example of Poussin's manner in the very late 'forties or early 'fifties, with severe classical composition and almost grotesque mask-like faces. It approaches most nearly to the drawings for the 'Judgment of Solomon' or the 'Conversion of St. Paul' (cf. Friedlaender, *Drawings*, i, p. 36f, Nos. 69, 70, 71. In composition it recalls the drawing of the 'Continence of Scipio' at Chantilly (cf. H. Malo, *Cent-deux dessins de Nicolas Poussin*, pl. 35).

221. The three Marys at the sepulchre.

Pl. 62. No. 4877A.

108 mm. × 140 mm. Black chalk.

This drawing was mounted on the same sheet as the head of an old man by Andrea Sacchi and formed part of the volume of Sacchi drawings. There is, however, no doubt that it is an original work by Poussin, dating from his last period. Other sketches with exactly the same thick, hesitant but expressive chalk line were produced by him in the 'fifties, particularly three for a 'Finding of Moses' in the Louvre and at Chantilly (cf. Friedlaender, *Drawings*, i, p. 6f, Nos. 6–8). No painting of this subject by Poussin is known. It is not unusual to find among the various great series of drawings by a single Italian master at Windsor works by other artists which were probably in the possession of the master to whom the volume is devoted. The Maratta series, for instance, contained several drawings by Sacchi and one original by Raphael. In view of Sacchi's position as representing the classical tradition in Roman seventeenth-century painting it is not at all unexpected that he should have owned a sketch by Poussin.

NICOLAS POUSSIN. (Attributed to.)

222. View of a hill-town near Rome.   *Pl. 70.* No. 6140.

208 mm. × 370 mm. Pen and bistre on brown paper. Inscribed: *G P.*

The exact site cannot be identified, but the town has the character of those in the Alban hills, or near Tivoli. It is of a type familiar in many landscapes by Gaspard Dughet.

The initials G P on the drawing presumably indicate an old attribution to this artist, but the landscape is so logically conceived and so clearly constructed, in almost mathematical forms, that it is hard to believe that it is by him. It is nearer in these respects to Nicolas Poussin, and certain details confirm the connexion with his hand. The use of rich bistre wash recalls his mythological drawings of the period about 1635, and the drawing of the shrubs is very close to similar passages in No. 187. The landscape drawings which can be attributed to Poussin with certainty are all drier in touch than this; but they date from a later period, from the end of the 'forties, and it is quite likely that the present drawing represents one of his early experiments in landscape, dating from the middle of the 'thirties.

NICOLAS POUSSIN. (Studio of.)

The following drawings were executed in Poussin's studio by his assistants and probably under his direct supervision. Many of them are connected with known designs by the artist himself.

A. Studio drawings connected with Poussin's work before 1641.

223. The Kingdom of Flora.   *Pl. 67.* No. 11878.

349 mm. × 476 mm. Pen and bistre wash over black chalk.

Literature: Bellori, *Vite*, p. 441.

Finished studio version of the composition shown in Poussin's drawing No. 169 above, but nearer in detail to the painting. It forms a series with Nos. 224, 225 below. Bellori describes the composition, but the description could apply equally to the painting or to this drawing. In view, however, of the fact that on the following pages he exactly describes Nos. 224, 225, after which no paintings by Poussin are known, it is quite likely that he actually had the drawing in mind.

224. Venus and Adonis hunting.   No. 11877.

350 mm. × 503 mm. Pen and bistre wash over black chalk.

II, 18—Literature: Bellori, *Vite*, p. 443; Friedlaender, *Burlington*, liv, p. 255.

The similarity in style and size to Nos. 223, 225 leaves no doubt that this drawing was intended to form one of the same series, although no original drawing or painting by Poussin is known of this composition. The subject is Venus and Adonis hunting (Ovid, *Met.*, x, 533) and not Diana and Actaeon as suggested by Friedlaender (*Burlington*, liv, p. 255). The drawing is exactly described by Bellori, who gives as its title 'La Tintura delle Rosa', owing to the legend that roses were coloured red by the blood which flowed from the foot of Venus when she was pricked by roses while hunting with Adonis.

225. 'La Tintura del Corallo.'   No. 11879.

351 mm. × 515 mm. Pen and bistre wash over black chalk.

Literature: Bellori, *Vite*, p. 443.

Finished studio version of the composition shown in Poussin's drawing No. 170 above. Forms a series with Nos. 223, 224. The composition is described by Bellori. He probably had in mind this drawing rather than No. 170 above.

226. Rinaldo and Armida.   *Pl. 66.* No. 11976.

250 mm. × 367 mm. Pen and bistre wash over black chalk.

Massimi 71—Literature: Bellori, *Vite*, p. 447; *F.A.Q.R.*, ii, p. 180; Friedlaender, *Burlington*, liv, p. 258.

Finished studio version almost identical with the painting for Stella (cf. No. 201 above). Bellori describes a composition which must be this drawing, though he gives no indication that he is not discussing a painting.

227. Three Satyrs.   No. 11992.

247 mm. × 318 mm. Round top. Pen and bistre over black chalk.

II, 34—Literature: Chamberlaine, pl. 47.

Finished studio drawing. Not connected with any painting, but belonging in general to the group of Bacchic compositions of the middle and late 'thirties.

228. Two Philosophers disputing.   No. 038.

131 mm. × 107 mm. Irregularly cut. Pen and bistre.

The subject may perhaps be 'Alexander and Aristotle'. The drawing is by the same studio hand as No. 229, and both these drawings are clearly related to No. 227. Probably dates from the late 'thirties.

229. *Recto:* Two Apostles.   No. 039.

136 mm. × 146 mm. Pen and bistre wash over red chalk.

Massimi 57—Literature: *F.A.Q.R.*, ii, p. 179.

This drawing is identified in the Massimi catalogue as representing Heracleitus and Democritus. This

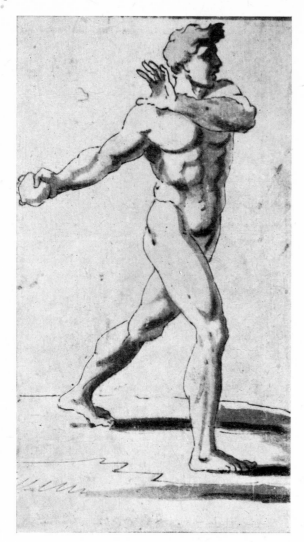

Fig. 5. NICOLAS POUSSIN (Studio):
Illustration to Leonardo da Vinci's *Trattato della
Pittura*. Catalogue No. 230

interpretation is, however, fanciful, and it seems more
likely that the figures are in reality those of two Apostles.
By the same hand as No. 228.

Verso: Fragments of three figures.

Pen and bistre over red chalk.

Perhaps studies for the same subject as the sketch on the
recto, but weaker.

Designs for plates in Leonardo da Vinci's *Trattato della
Pittura*, 1651.

230. 113 mm. × 63 mm.   *Fig. 5.* No. 11953.
For plate to ch. 182, p. 51 (right-hand figure only).

231. 130 mm. × 148 mm. Numbered: 2.   No. 11955.
For plate to ch. 197, p. 55.

232. 129 mm. × 78 mm. Numbered: 3.   No. 11966.
For plate to ch. 200, p. 56.

233. 129 mm. × 81 mm. Numbered: 4.   No. 11964.
For plate to ch. 201, p. 57.

234. 131 mm. × 80 mm. Numbered: 5. Figures: 202 in
top right-hand corner.   No. 11965.
For plate to ch. 202, p. 58.

235. 115 mm. × 54 mm. Numbered: 1.   No. 11954.
For plate to ch. 203, p. 59.

236. 130 mm. × 69 mm. Numbered: 6.   No. 11963.
For plate to ch. 231, p. 65.

237. 121 mm. × 127 mm. Numbered: 7.   No. 11959.
For plate to ch. 232, p. 66.

238. 138 mm. × 88 mm. Numbered: 8.   No. 11961.
For plate to ch. 233, p. 67.

239. 139 mm. × 208 mm. Numbered: 9.   No. 11957.
For plate to ch. 235, p. 69.

240. 126 mm. × 133 mm. Numbered: 10.   No. 11956.
For plate to ch. 261, p. 75.

241. 144 mm. × 142 mm. Numbered: 11.   No. 11958.
For plate to ch. 263, p. 76.

242. 159 mm. × 170 mm. Numbered: 12.   No. 11951.
For plate to ch. 268, p. 77.

243. 120 mm. × 110 mm. Numbered: 13.   No. 11960.
For plate to ch. 295, p. 85.

244. 111 mm. × 51 mm. Numbered: 14.   No. 11952.
For plate to ch. 301, p. 89.

245. 128 mm. × 78 mm. Numbered: 15.   No. 11962.
For plate to ch. 360, p. 110.

All in pen and bistre with blue-grey wash.

These sixteen drawings are closely related to the engravings in the edition of Leonardo's *Trattato della
Pittura*, published by du Fresne in Paris in Italian and
French in 1651. The engravings were based on drawings
made by Poussin which in their turn were inspired by
Leonardo's text and by the small sketches in the manuscript in the Barberini library (reproduced in Manzi's
edition of the *Trattato*, 1817).

Poussin made his drawings at the request of Cassiano del
Pozzo, and it is known that several sets of copies of
manuscript illustrations were later made for other con-
noisseurs. The problem of these various versions has been
discussed by Hautecœur (cf. Grautoff, *Nicolas Poussin*,
1914, i, p. 371ff.), but he did not know the Windsor set,
and certain other facts escaped his notice.

The only manuscript with illustrations of which one can
speak with confidence is that in the Hermitage, described
at length by Hautecœur. The inscription on the fly-leaf
proves that it is the volume given by Cassiano del Pozzo
to Chantelou in 1640 when the latter visited Rome to

accompany Poussin to Paris. This is undoubtedly the copy on which the printed version was based, though the engraver has taken liberties with the drawings, and the numbering of the chapters has been altered (e.g. the Hermitage drawing to ch. 202 is numbered 203, that to 233 is numbered 230). Hautecœur assumes that the Hermitage drawings are the originals, but it seems more likely that they are copies made for Chantelou at the order of Cassiano del Posso. It is intrinsically probable that Cassiano would have kept the originals in his own collection, and further, the handling of both line and wash in the Hermitage drawings suggests a fluent Italian imitator rather than Poussin himself.

In addition to Cassiano and Chantelou we know that Sandrart was given by Poussin a copy of the manuscript which probably included the drawings (cf. *Teutsche Akademie*, ed. Peltzer, 1925, p. 411), and that Félibien caused copies of both to be made when he was in Rome in 1648 (cf. *Entretiens*, iv, p. 22). Hautecœur (*loc. cit.*, p. 376), moreover, mentions a copy belonging to Noailles in 1745 which was said to have belonged to Cassiano, Chantelou, Massimi, Crozat and Thiers. This is evidently a confusion, since Massimi is very unlikely to have owned the Chantelou copy, which left Italy in 1640. It may, however, indicate that he owned another copy.

There were, therefore, probably at least four or five copies in existence in the seventeenth century, of which only one can be traced definitely today. Hautecœur indicates the existence of the following during the last 150 years:

(1) A volume belonging to the Comtesse de Béarn in 1914.

(2) A volume in the James Edwards sale, 5.4.1815, lot 377, later belonging to Payne and Esdaile.

(3) The Noailles volume, bought at the 1795 sale by 'M. J. de P'.

(4) A volume with outline drawings mentioned by Gault de St. Germain.

The Windsor set must originally have been made to accompany a manuscript copy of the *Trattato*, but there is reason to think that the drawings were probably separated from the manuscript before the end of the seventeenth century. The set is incomplete and does not include drawings for the plates illustrating chs. 89, 181, 209, which are also based on Poussin's designs (the other plates—geometrical and anatomical, etc.—are not after him). On the other hand, they are numbered consecutively from 1 to 15 (No. 230 having no number) in a seventeenth-century hand. The missing drawings would probably come at various points in this series, and it looks therefore as though the numbers were put on when the set was already incomplete, and therefore probably separated from the manuscript. Moreover the number 202 on No. 234 corresponds to the chapter in the printed version, not to that in the Hermitage manuscript. It

seems probable, therefore, that the drawings were numbered in the seventeenth century according to the printed copy (though No. 235, numbered 1, comes out of its proper order).

It is possible to fix with some accuracy the date at which Poussin originally made his illustrations to the *Trattato*. Two of the drawings, Nos. 230, 240, are almost identical with figures in the 'Pyrrhus' in the Louvre (Grautoff, No. 57, cf. No. 189 above), which must have been painted about 1635. Another, No. 243, is connected with a figure in the 'Manna', also in the Louvre (Grautoff, No. 90) painted in 1638–9. Moreover Sandrart, to whom Poussin gave a copy of the *Trattato*, left Rome in 1635. The original drawings, therefore, cannot have been made after 1635, and, in view of their connections with paintings of 1635 and 1638, they are unlikely to have been made much earlier.

The Windsor drawings are too mechanical to be the originals by Poussin himself. The outline is hard and insensitive and in many cases the foreground is indicated by a somewhat meaningless scribble. On the other hand, certain details, particularly of plants and trees, are nearer to Poussin in handling in the Windsor than in the Hermitage series. The general character of the former suggests that they are by a French member of Poussin's studio working about 1640.

A single undoubtedly original drawing by Poussin indirectly connected with the *Trattato* is known, namely one of a horse in Stockholm, related to No. 242. The Stockholm drawing is an almost exact rendering of the horse from the statue of Marcus Aurelius on the Capitol. It does not agree exactly with the drawings or the engraving for the *Trattato*, but it is close enough to suggest that it may have been used by Poussin as the basis for his theoretical drawing. The Stockholm horse and the drawing on the verso of the same sheet are both in the style of the middle 'thirties, and, therefore, date from the time when Poussin was probably working on the Leonardo illustrations.

B. Studio drawings made during the visit to Paris, 1641–42.

During his visit to Paris in 1641–42, Poussin was compelled to undertake a series of commissions of a type entirely uncongenial to him. These consisted of large altar-pieces and decorative paintings for the King, Richelieu and de Noyers; designs for frontispieces to be used for books printed at the Royal printing press; and finally the scheme for decorating the Long Gallery at the Louvre.

These commissions were of such a kind that Poussin could not possibly undertake them entirely himself, and consequently we find that during his time in Paris he made greater use of assistants than when he was working at his own discretion in Rome. In his letters from Paris he refers to 'la brigade' of artists working with him, of whom his brother-in-law, Jean Dughet, and his friend,

E

Jean Lemaire were the most important, but which included also Jean Mosnier and Nicolas de la Fage who came with him from Rome, and probably also Salomon Girard, Jacques Stella and Remy Vuibert, apart from sculptors and stucco-workers (cf. Grautoff, *Nicolas Poussin*, i, pp. 194, 202). His use of these assistants is confirmed by the existence of a large series of highly finished studio drawings made during this period. These were probably intended as designs to be shown to the patron for his approval (cf. Nos. 246, 247), or as actual working drawings for decoration (Nos. 252–255), or as models for the engraver (Nos. 248–250).

It is impossible to attribute these drawings to any of the artists named above, though certain groups can be identified as being by a single hand.

246. Moses and the Burning Bush.   No. 11907.

256 mm. × 218 mm. Oval. Pen and bistre wash.

Massimi 49—Literature: *F.A.Q.R.*, ii, p. 178; Friedlaender, *Burlington*, liv, p. 256; Friedlaender, *Drawings*, i, p. 10, A4.

Finished studio drawing for the painting executed in Paris in 1641 for Richelieu, now in Copenhagen. Another similar drawing, also studio work, is in the Louvre (cf. Friedlaender, *Drawings*, i, p. 10, A5).

247. The Institution of the Sacrament.   No. 11876.

558 mm. × 403 mm. Pen and bistre wash over black chalk on buff paper.

II, 9—Literature: *F.A.Q.R.*, iii, p. 110; Friedlaender, *Drawings*, i, p. 49.

Finished studio drawing for the painting executed in 1641 for the chapel at St. Germain, now in the Louvre (Grautoff, No. 100).

248. Frontispiece to the Works of Virgil.   No. 11948.

374 mm. × 240 mm. Pen and bistre wash over black chalk on greenish paper.

II, 11—Literature: *F.A.Q.R.*, iii, p. 110.

Exact preliminary drawing for the engraving by Mellan which appeared as frontispiece to the edition of Virgil published by the Imprimerie Royale in 1641 (Andresen, No. 432). The composition is described by Bellori (*Vite*, p. 430). Poussin sent off two finished drawings of this composition on 10th April, 1641, one to de Noyers, and one to Chantelou (cf. *Correspondance*, pp. 53, 55). The present drawing is probably one of these.

In the engraving the head of Virgil was changed, since critics had protested against his being represented as bearded.

249. Frontispiece to the Works of Horace.   No. 11949.

373 mm. × 232 mm. Black chalk—Inscribed: *N. poussin faciebat*.

II, 12—Literature: *F.A.Q.R.*, iii, p. 110.

Exact preliminary drawing for Mellan's engraving for the edition of Horace's works published by the Imprimerie Royale in 1642 (Andresen, No. 433). The composition is described by Bellori (*Vite*, p. 430). The present drawing may be that referred to by Poussin in a letter of 20th March, 1642 (*Correspondance*, p. 121). In technique and style it is unlike any of the other finished studio drawings.

Hautecœur (Grautoff, *Nicolas Poussin*, i, p. 379) mentions another drawing for this frontispiece in the Hermitage. It was, however, not to be seen there in 1935.

250. Illustration to the *Hesperides* of Ferrari.   No. 11950.

305 mm. × 212 mm. Pen and yellowish wash, heightened with white, on blue paper. Inscribed: *Nico. Poussin Inv.*

II, 23.

Finished studio drawing for one of the plates in Ferrari's *Hesperides sive de malorum aureorum cultura et usu* (Rome, 1646). Engraved by Cornelius Bloemaert (Andresen, No. 435). Poussin frequently mentions the book in his letters written from Paris in 1642 (*Correspondance*, p. 110, etc.), and the drawing was no doubt executed at that time. A very similar studio drawing for the same composition is in the Louvre.

251. Scipio Africanus and the Pirates.   *Pl. 65.* No. 0698.

331 mm. × 468 mm. Pen and bistre wash over black chalk.

II, 15—Literature: *F.A.Q.R.*, iii, p. 110.

Wrongly described in *F.A.Q.R.* as 'Germanicus pardoning the Mutineers'. Finished studio drawing based on sketches such as No. 211 above. Probably the drawing executed for Cardinal Barberini in Paris in 1642.

This is perhaps the finest of all the studio drawings, and certain parts of it, particularly the ships and figures in the distance and the statues in the niches, are so vigorous that they may have been drawn by Poussin himself. On the other hand the architecture, which is ruled in, and the foreground figures are much weaker.

Studies for the Decoration of the Long Gallery at the Louvre.

One of the principal tasks for which Poussin was called to Paris was the decoration of the Long Gallery of the Louvre, which had been left incomplete. This work, uncongenial in itself, was made harder by the fact that some parts had already been executed by Lemercier. In 1642 Poussin abandoned the work and returned to Rome; but he had already produced a large number of designs for individual panels of decoration, which are known to us in the studio drawings made for them. Four of these drawings are at Windsor, some in the Louvre, and a large number of others in the Hermitage. All these designs are in direct imitation of ancient bas-reliefs, and were no doubt to be painted in grisaille to look like marbles. For an original drawing for one of these compositions cf. No. 214 above. Some of these designs were engraved by J. Pesne in a volume entitled: *Herculis Labores*, 1678 (cf. No. 256 below).

252. The Infant Hercules killing the serpents sent by Juno. No. 11970.

162 mm. × 432 mm. Pen and bistre wash over black chalk on buff paper, heightened with white. Squared.

II, 36.

To the same series as this belong Louvre 32441, 32443, and Hermitage 7995, 7999, 8000, 8004, 8008, 8009.

253. Hermes, Apollo and Iris. No. 11969.

Circular. 278 mm. in diameter. Pen and bistre wash over black chalk, heightened with white, on buff paper. Squared.

II, 32.

Identical in technique with No. 252. Other drawings in the same series are Hermitage 7994, 7996, 7997, 7998.

254. Hercules killing the Centaurs. No. 11973.

Circular. 262 mm. in diameter. Pen and bistre wash over black chalk, heightened with white, on blue-green paper. Squared. Inscribed in an eighteenth-century hand: *n. Poussin*.

II, 30.

To the same series belong the following drawing No. 255 and Hermitage 8001, 8002.

255. Hercules and the Erymanthean Boar.

Pl. 57. No. 11972.

218 mm. × 218 mm. The drawing circular. Pen and bistre wash over black chalk, heightened with white, on blue-green paper. Squared.

II, 31.

Identical in technique with No. 254 and forming part of the same series.

256. Hercules supporting the World. No. 11971.

236 mm. × 181 mm. Pen and bistre wash.

II, 33b.

A studio drawing connected with the decoration of the Long Gallery but quite different from Nos. 252–255, and more freely drawn. The figure appears exactly, in reverse, in the engraving of Hercules and Atlas in J. Pesne's *Herculis Labores*, 1678.

C. Studio drawings connected with Poussin's work after 1642.

257. Cupid on horseback. No. 11968.

Transferred to No. 212a.

258. The Body of Darius. No. 11989.

259 mm. × 410 mm. Pen and bistre wash on blue paper.

Massimi 65—Literature: *F.A.Q.R.*, ii, p. 180; Friedlaender, *Burlington*, liv, p. 257.

Sisygambis, the mother of Darius, receives the body of her son sent to her by Alexander after he had been murdered by Bessus. Free studio drawing, not connected with any painting.

259. The Ecstasy of St. Mary Magdalene. No. 11908.

258 mm. × 186 mm. Pen and bistre wash.

II, 10—Literature: *F.A.Q.R.*, iii, p. 110; Friedlaender, *Drawings*, i, p. 38, A18.

An elaborate studio drawing not connected with any composition known in painting.

260. Ordination. No. 11899.

198 mm. × 327 mm. Pen and bistre wash, lightly squared.

Massimi 60—Literature: *F.A.Q.R.*, ii, p. 180; Friedlaender, *Burlington*, liv, p. 257; Friedlaender, *Drawings*, i, p. 47, A21.

Closely connected with the 'Ordination' from the second series of Sacraments, painted for Chantelou in 1647 (Grautoff, No. 121). This and the two following drawings Nos. 261, 262 are very close to Poussin's manner and may possibly be originals, but a certain weakness in the detail of the drawing (e.g. in hands and faces) makes it more likely that they are the work of a very competent pupil. The present drawing is attractive in its rather colourful wash, but very weak in the awkward proportions of its figures. An original drawing by Poussin for the 'Ordination' is in the Pierpont Morgan Library (cf. Friedlaender, *Drawings*, i, p. 46, No. 98).

261. Confirmation. *Pl. 69.* No. 11898.

186 mm. × 287 mm. Pen and dark bistre wash. Lightly squared.

Massimi 62—Literature: *F.A.Q.R.*, ii, p. 180; Friedlaender, *Burlington*, liv, p. 257; Friedlaender, *Drawings*, i, p. 44, A20.

A more finished study for the same painting as No. 215. Probably like the last drawing by a very competent member of Poussin's studio.

262. Moses trampling on Pharaoh's crown.

Pl. 68. No. 11885.

161 mm. × 253 mm. Pen and bistre wash; squared.

II, 5b—Literature: *F.A.Q.R.*, iii, p. 108; Friedlaender, *Drawings*, i, p. 7, No. 9.

A finished study for the painting executed for Cardinal Massimi (Grautoff, No. 110). In Friedlaender, *Drawings*, this was accepted, with reservations, as original, but it seems more likely that it is by a very able follower, like the last two drawings. It probably dates from the late 'forties, not from the early 'fifties as suggested in Friedlaender, *Drawings*.

It is curious that, though it is a sketch for a painting commissioned by Cardinal Massimi, this drawing did not form part of the Massimi volume.

263. Roman relief.　　　　　　　No. 11880.

96 mm. × 497 mm. Pen and bistre wash. In lower right-hand corner the figures: 267.

II, 35—Literature: C. Robert, *Die Antiken Sarkophag-Reliefs*, 1890, ii, p. 193.

After a Roman sarcophagus in the Villa Pamfili, of which other drawings are also known (cf. Robert, *op. cit.*, ii, pl. LX, No. 184), one in the Pozzo volumes at Windsor. The scenes depicted are from *The Seven against Thebes*. The number 267 is in the same hand as those on certain Pozzo drawings, and it is likely that this drawing also belonged to his collection. It may have been separated from its companions either because the collection already contained a duplicate of the same relief, or because it was considered to be of particular importance as a supposed work of Poussin. It is probably the drawing in the second Poussin volume at Windsor described, incorrectly, in the manuscript catalogue, as 'Scenes from the Trojan War'.

264. Medea killing her children.　*Pl. 61.* No. 11893.

257 mm. × 200 mm. Pen and bistre wash over black chalk.

II, 25—Literature: Bellori, *Vite*, p. 449; Chamberlaine, pl. 55; Friedlaender, *Burlington*, liv, p. 127.

Studio drawing based on Poussin's sketch No. 217 above. Probably by the same hand as No. 265.

265. Alpheus and Arethusa.　　　No. 11977.

305 mm. × 222 mm. Pen and bistre wash.

Massimi 25—Literature: *F.A.Q.R.*, i, p. 272; Friedlaender, *Burlington*, liv, p. 254.

The story is told by Ovid (*Met.*, V, 595). The nymph Arethusa, pursued by the river-god Alpheus, prayed to Diana, who concealed her from her pursuer by a cloud. Friedlaender (*Burlington*, liv, p. 254) regards this as belonging to the Marino series, but it differs from them entirely in technique and style. It is a studio drawing, probably by the same hand as No. 264. No original drawing or painting by Poussin of this subject is known.

266. Christ healing the blind men.　No. 11900.

144 mm. × 186 mm. Pen and bistre wash.

II, 5a—Literature: *F.A.Q.R.*, iii, p. 107; Friedlaender, *Drawings*, i, p. 32, A12.

Studio drawing connected with the painting executed in 1650 (Grautoff, No. 140). Another similar sketch is No. 267 below, and an original sketch by Poussin for the same composition is No. 219 above.

267. Christ healing the blind men.　No. 11901.

135 mm. × 171 mm. Pen and bistre wash.

Massimi 58—Literature: *F.A.Q.R.*, ii, p. 179; Friedlaender, *Burlington*, liv. p. 257; Friedlaender, *Drawings*, i, p. 32, A11.

Like the last drawing, a studio sketch for the painting.

268. The Altar of Priapus.　　　No. 11974.

203 mm. × 276 mm. Pen and bistre with yellow wash.

Massimi 15—Literature: *F.A.Q.R.*, i, p. 270; Friedlaender, *Burlington*, liv, p. 253.

On the left are a cupid and a nymph seated on a dolphin making love; in the centre a youth leads a bashful maiden to the altar; on the right an old woman and an old man with a lamp attend them. Various Priapic attributes are visible. The whole drawing is made as if after a fragment of ancient sculpture, but it may well be a pastiche after the antique.

A weak studio drawing, probably by the same hand as No. 269.

269. A Bishop.　　　　　　　　No. 11978.

145 mm. × 168 mm. Irregularly cut. Pen and bistre with yellow wash.

Literature: Friedlaender, *Drawings*, i, p. 17, B6.

It has been suggested without great plausibility that the drawing represents Eli and Samuel. Identical in technique and style with No. 268, and probably by the same hand.

270. The Creation of Sun and Moon.　No. 11998.

180 mm. × 201 mm. Pen and bistre wash, heightened with white, on blue-green paper.

II, 1a—Literature: *F.A.Q.R.*, iii, p. 106.

A copy by a member of Poussin's Roman circle after an engraving from Raphael's painting of the same subject in the Loggie.

271. Roman Relief.　　　　　　No. 11881.

205 mm. × 458 mm. Pen and grey wash. In lower right-hand corner figures: 164.

After a relief formerly in the Villa Medici, Rome, and now in the Uffizi (cf. engraving in reverse in Bartoli, *Admiranda Romanorum antiquitatum ac veteris sculpturæ vestigia*, 1693, pl. 82).

The number in the bottom right-hand corner indicates that, like No. 263, this drawing belonged to the volumes made for Cassiano del Pozzo.

NICOLAS POUSSIN (School of).

Under this heading are grouped drawings traditionally attributed to Poussin or closely related with his manner, which, however, are not connected with compositions by him and do not appear to have been executed actually in his studio.

272. The Virgin and her companions. No. 11883.

172 mm. × 259 mm. Pen and bistre wash.

Literature: Friedlaender, *Burlington*, liv, pp. 127, 257; *Seventeenth Century Art*, R.A., 1938, p. 175, No. 520.

A free version of Guido Reni's painting of this subject now in the Hermitage (No. 191). Probably by an Italian imitator of Poussin. This drawing is wrongly identified by Friedlaender as number 68 of the Massimi volume (cf. No. 179).

273. Landscape with classical buildings. No. 11996.

246 mm. × 367 mm. Pen and bistre wash over black chalk.

Probably by a French imitator of Poussin's classical landscapes, about 1660–1680.

274. View of Italian farm buildings. *Pl. 71.* No. 6141.

268 mm. × 311 mm. Pen and bistre, with traces of black chalk.

Traditionally attributed to Gaspard Dughet, but quite unlike him in style. A very unusual drawing which in some ways recalls draughtsmen of the sixteenth century. The classical arrangement of the composition, however, seems to show the influence of Poussin. The drawing is related to the landscape backgrounds in certain drawings of religious subjects by Poussin dating from the late 'forties and early 'fifties. Probably by a French imitator of about that period working in Italy.

275. The Martyrdom of St. Erasmus. No. 11991.

320 mm. × 200 mm. Pen and bistre with some red chalk, heightened with white. Squared.

II, 24—Literature: Friedlaender, *Drawings*, i, p. 39.

A free variant after Poussin's altarpiece for St. Peter's, now in the Vatican (Grautoff, No. 15). By a feeble imitator.

276. Three studies of heads and a foot. No. 11929.

95 mm. × 128 mm. Black chalk.

II, 22.

Copies of details from paintings (cf. Nos. 282, 283). Probably by an Italian artist of Cassiano del Pozzo's circle. According to the manuscript catalogue the foot is after Giulio Romano.

E*

277. Heads of Children. No. 11928.

92 mm. × 150 mm. Pen and bistre.

Massimi 55—Literature: *F.A.Q.R.*, ii, p. 179; Friedlaender, *Burlington*, liv, p. 257.

According to the Massimi catalogue these are the portraits drawn from life by Poussin of the children of Carlo Antonio del Pozzo, brother of Poussin's patron Cassiano. The drawing, however, is of very poor quality and bears little resemblance to Poussin's style. Moreover the heads appear to be ideal studies in expression rather than portraits. In this case, therefore, as in others, we are forced to set aside the testimony of the catalogue. The drawing is probably by an Italian member of Poussin's circle.

278. *Recto:* Death of Cato the Younger. No. 11994.

192 mm. × 291 mm. Pen and bistre heightened with white on blue paper.

III, 4a.

This drawing is not connected with Poussin's sketch of the same subject described under No. 206. It seems to be by a French imitator. Individual figures are connected with Poussin's paintings of the late 'forties.

Verso: Rough sketches of heads.

Pen and bistre.

NICOLAS POUSSIN (After).

279. Portrait of Nicolas Poussin. No. 11993.

225 mm. × 268 mm. Red chalk.

Massimi 1—Literature: *F.A.Q.R.*, i, p. 268; Friedlaender, *Burlington*, liv, p. 253.

A copy of the self-portrait in the Louvre, or from the engraving after it. Made probably in the late seventeenth century, as a frontispiece to the Massimi volume.

280. Coriolanus. No. 11891.

162 mm. × 238 mm. Pen and bistre wash over black chalk.

III, 4b.

Probably a copy after a lost study for the painting executed for the Marquis d'Hauterive, now at Les Andelys (Grautoff, No. 68). It is just possible, however, that the pencil under-drawing, which is of far better quality than the pen drawing, may be original.

281. Landscape with a woman washing her feet. No. 5723.

266 mm. × 420 mm. Pen and bistre with bistre and grey wash.

After the landscape mentioned by Félibien (*Entretiens*, p. 62) which is now in the collection of Mrs. H. S. Southam, Casa Loma, Ottawa (cf. *Art News*, March 1940, p. 12). For a copy cf. Grautoff, No. 143.

282. Studies of heads.   No. 11930.

90 mm. × 141 mm. Black chalk.

283. Studies of heads.   No. 11932.

79 mm. × 133 mm. Black chalk.

One of these two drawings is II, 27.

Copies of four heads in Poussin's painting of the 'Woman taken in Adultery' (Grautoff, No. 148). Perhaps made as models for some of the many engravings after heads taken from Poussin's compositions.

284. Studies of heads.   No. 11931.

87 mm. × 205 mm. Black chalk.

Massimi 56—Literature: *F.A.Q.R.*, ii, p. 179; Friedlaender, *Burlington*, liv, p. 257.

The Massimi catalogue identifies these trivial sketches as a series of ancient philosophers, orators and poets. They seem, however, rather to be a series of copies made after heads by Poussin by an artist belonging to the circle of Cassiano del Pozzo. The head in profile in the middle seems to be a copy of one in a sheet of sketches by Poussin in the Louvre (cf. Friedlaender, *Drawings*, i, p. 48, No. 101).

JACQUES ROUSSEAU (1630–1693).

Seven classical landscapes.

285.   No. 6566.

293 mm. × 429 mm. Indian ink wash. Inscribed in an eighteenth-century hand: *James Rousseau.*

286.   No. 6567.

300 mm. × 433 mm. Indian ink wash. Inscribed faintly in the same hand: *(James) Rousseau.*

287.   No. 6568.

293 mm. × 428 mm. Indian ink wash with traces of red chalk.

288.   No. 6569.

293 mm. × 428 mm. Indian ink wash.

289.   No. 6570.

293 mm. × 427 mm. Black chalk, pen and bistre with Indian ink wash.

290.   No. 6571.

295 mm. × 428 mm. Black chalk, pen and bistre with Indian ink wash.

291.   No. 6572.

293 mm. × 430 mm. Indian ink wash.

These seven drawings, though varying slightly in technique, are all similar in size and general character and form a single series. The style and the use of the English form of the Christian name on No. 285 indicate clearly the attribution to the Jacques Rousseau

who worked in England from 1690 to 1693. Five of his architectural landscapes survive as *dessus-de-portes* at Hampton Court.

292. Classical landscape.   No. 5794.

270 mm. × 373 mm. Pen and bistre wash over black chalk.

293. Landscape with peasants.   No. 5795.

285 mm. × 389 mm. Pen and bistre over black chalk.

294. Classical landscape.   No. 5796.

318 mm. × 424 mm. Pen and bistre over black chalk.

295. *Recto:* River and waterfall.   No. 5812.

284 mm. × 396 mm. Pen and bistre wash.

Verso: River bank.

Black and red chalk and bistre wash.

The first three form a series, and, together with the recto drawing of No. 295, are so close in style to the seven landscapes described above that they can be confidently ascribed to Rousseau. The drawing on the verso of No. 295 is more Flemish in character, but is probably by the same hand.

ISRAEL SILVESTRE (1621–1691).

296. The Grotto at Meudon.   *Pl. 95.* No. 13101.

74 mm. × 182 mm. Pen and bistre. Outlines gone over with stylus.

An exact study for the engraving by Silvestre (Faucheux, 48 (8)). The grotto was built by Philibert Delorme and was the principal ornament of the gardens at Meudon.

ISRAEL SILVESTRE (Attributed to.)

297. View of S. Giovanni dei Fiorentini, Rome.

      No. 5820.

190 mm. × 267 mm. Black and red chalk and grey wash.

The view is taken from the south of the church and shows the Tiber, with the Ospedale di S. Spirito in the background.

The curious mixture of media, the rather coarse wash foreground and the precise drawing in black chalk justify an attribution to Silvestre.

CHARLES SIMONNEAU (1645–1728).

298. *Recto:* Two sketches of a fortified farmhouse and trees.   *Pl. 97.* No. 6599.

185 mm. × 310 mm. Pen and bistre over red chalk. Inscribed: *Charles Simonneau faccit.*

Verso: A waterfall and trees.

Pen and bistre over red chalk.

Both these drawings represent Italian scenes—the verso sketch is probably inspired by the falls of Tivoli—and they provide the only existing evidence to show that Simonneau visited Italy. He is, moreover, principally famous as an engraver after the work of others, and these experiments in original landscape drawings reveal an apparently unknown aspect of his art.

299. Landscape with an Italian hill town.   No. 6598.

178 mm. × 304 mm. Pen and bistre over red chalk.

The identity in technique and style of draughtsmanship with the last drawing justifies the attribution of this sketch also to Simonneau. In view of its subject it must also date from his Italian visit.

FRANÇOIS SPIERRE (1639–1681).

300. Allegorical subject.   No. 4500.

245 mm. × 323 mm. Black chalk heightened with white. Inscribed: *di Monsù Spierre*.

Identical in composition and scale with an engraving by Spierre after Ciro Ferri. The subject can be elucidated from the inscription below the engraving as follows. On the left sits a youth representing Human Intelligence (*ingenium*). Under the tuition of Philosophy, who sits with him, he treads under foot the serpent of Falsehood. On the right three maidens, representing the three branches of philosophy, weave for him a crown from the roses of Truth and the thorns of Difficulty. Above two putti carry a ribbon with the inscription: *Educent bene culta rosas*.

The old attribution to Spierre and the fact that the drawing has been pressed through indicate that this is Spierre's preparation for the engraving and not the original drawing by Ferri.

ANONYMOUS ARTIST (c. 1650).

301. Landscape.   *Pl. 98.* No. 6576.

270 mm. × 413 mm. Pen and bistre with water-colours. Inscribed: *le palais sur le mont*, and bearing abbreviated colour notes: *VB, VR, VJ, VJR, J clair*.

This somewhat fantastic landscape shows a Palladian villa poised on the top of a steep and rocky hill. In the foreground are trees and Italian farm buildings. The draughtsmanship seems almost to indicate an Italian artist, and the use of full water-colours as opposed to bistre shows strong Flemish influence. On the other hand the inscription makes it almost impossible to avoid the conclusion that the drawing is by a Frenchman, and suggests a date about the middle of the century. From the mountainous landscape and the Palladian architecture it looks as though the artist was familiar with northern Italy.

The initials *V, B, J, R* in the notes on the drawing presumably stand for *vert, brun, jaune* and *rouge*.

ANONYMOUS ARTIST (c. 1650).

302. Four studies of Chinese men.   *Pl. 99.* No. 13073.

299 mm. × 189 mm. Black chalk on buff paper. Inscribed: *blanc, rouge, dens la joue* (?).

A full-length study and three heads. The features make it evident that the men are Orientals, and not Europeans wearing Chinese dress; and the inscription shows that the artist was French. Visitors from China to Europe in the first half of the seventeenth century were excessively rare, and it is impossible that a Frenchman could have seen four such visitors at once. The drawing must, therefore, either be the work of an artist who went to the East, or a copy after a Chinese painting. There were artists who travelled to China with missionaries or traders at this period, but none of them was French, and none was of the calibre to have executed this drawing. It is, therefore, almost certain that the drawing must be a copy after a Chinese original; and several details support this theory. The attitude of the man on the left, with his hands in his sleeves, is one which frequently occurs in Oriental art, and the lines of his drapery follow the traditional curves. The quality of the line has even a Chinese flavour. It is known that Chinese paintings existed in Europe at this time, and Feuillet de Conches mentions a series of portraits representing the Chinese Imperial Family in the Palazzo Barberini which are said to have been presented to Urban VIII (cf. *Revue Contemporaine*, xxv, 1856, p. 251). It is quite possible that the French draughtsman may have seen this volume, or a similar one, in Rome. If the drawing is in fact a copy after a Chinese original it is much the earliest example of this type of Oriental influence in French art.

ANONYMOUS ARTIST (c. 1654–1661).

303. Louis XIV and Mazarin at the Siege of Arras (1654).   No. 01183.

286 mm. × 456 mm. Pen and bistre with some black chalk. Inscribed on mount in late eighteenth-century hand: *Dessin D'Ant F. S. Van der Meulen.* Collector's mark: *Theodore Karjavine*.

The town in the background can be identified as Arras by a comparison with Stefano della Bella's engraving of the siege of 1640 (Jombert, 236) and the engravings of the siege of 1654 by Cochin, Fresne and others after Beaulieu. The figure of the young Louis XIV on horseback and that of Mazarin can be identified in the right foreground, and show that the subject is the siege of 1654, in one of the first campaigns at which Louis was present in person. The town, defended by the French under the governor Schulemberg, was besieged by the Spanish army under Condé, but was relieved by another French force commanded by Turenne. The flags of the Spanish besiegers, with their St. Andrew's cross, can be seen at various points outside the city, and the main French relieving force with its St. George's cross can be seen on the left near the foreground. The drawing bears no resemblance to the free Flemish style of van der Meulen, the attribution indicated by the old inscription, and is too crude to be by him or any of the other principal battle-painters of Louis XIV. The large scale of the foreground figures suggests an artist of an earlier generation, such as the author of the 'Battle of Breisach', engraved anonymously in the *Campagnes de Louis XIII*. This stylistic point, taken together with the prominence given to the figure of Mazarin, indicates that the composition was designed soon after the date of the battle and before the death of the Cardinal in 1661. The drawing itself is probably a later copy.

The collector's mark is not mentioned by Lugt, but is probably that of Theodore van Karajan (1810–1873), a Viennese collector (cf. Lugt, *Les Marques de collections de dessins et d'estampes*, 1921, No. 2701).

ANONYMOUS
ARTIST (1655–1660).
304. Portrait of Catherine de Menneville.
Fig. 6. No. 13244.

Fig. 6. ANONYMOUS ARTIST, 1655–60: Portrait of Catherine de Menneville. Catalogue No. 304

335 mm. × 234 mm. Gouache and gold paint on vellum.

A half-length portrait in an oval frame on which is the inscription: OC *de Maneville Fille d'Honneur de la Reyne*. Below are the figures of Juno, Venus and Minerva; above fly eight cherubs. All these figures carry scrolls with laudatory quatrains in honour of the sitter. The green background may be a later addition.

The sitter is Catherine de Menneville (1636–69), daughter of Louis de Roncherolles, Seigneur d'Azouville, and one of the most celebrated beauties of the French Court, c. 1655–60. She is mentioned by Madame de la Fayette in the *Histoire de Henriette d'Angleterre* (ed. E. Asse, 1890, p. 45), and by Mlle. de Montpensier (*Mémoires*, ed. Chéruel, 1891, iii, p. 114), who saw her among the ladies-in-waiting to Anne of Austria in 1657. She was engaged to the Duc de Damville, but the marriage never took place. She was dismissed from the Court in 1661 after the arrest of Fouquet among whose papers were found letters which proved that she had been his mistress. Details of her career are given by Chéruel in his edition of the *Mémoires de Mlle. de Montpensier* quoted above (iii, p. 598). Her beauty was praised by Racine in a letter to La Fontaine. (*Ibid.*, p. 590.)

ANONYMOUS ARTIST (c. 1660).
305. Susannah and the Elders.   No. 6187.

158 mm. × 193 mm. Pen and bistre with blue wash heightened with white on blue paper.

A drawing of too poor quality to admit of definite attribution. Probably by a provincial artist working about 1660. Possibly by the same hand as a drawing formerly in the Oppenheimer Collection attributed tentatively to Hilaire Pader of Toulouse (illustrated in E. Panofsky, *Hercules am Scheidewege*, 1930, pl. liii).

ANONYMOUS
ARTIST (1660–1670).
306. The Saving of the Infant Pyrrhus.   No. 3523.

256 mm. × 406 mm. Pen and bistre with grey wash heightened with white.

The artist was no doubt inspired to choose this rather rare subject by Poussin's well-known painting for which drawings exist at Windsor (cf. No. 189 above). The clumsy drawing of the figures and the more skilful treatment of the background suggest that this drawing is by a painter primarily interested in landscape. Probably by one of the imitators of Poussin working in the circle of the Paris Academy about 1660–70.

ANONYMOUS ARTIST (c. 1660–1680).
307. The Exposure of Moses.   No. 6186.

240 mm. × 324 mm. Pen and bistre wash over black chalk, heightened with white.

The style of this drawing suggests the circle of the Corneille family, the closest parallel being a drawing by Michel Corneille the Younger (1641–1708) in the Louvre, No. 2463.

EIGHTEENTH CENTURY

HYACINTHE BASSINET (working 1762).
308. A View of Winchester Palace.   *Fig. 7.* No. 17168.
141 mm. × 253 mm. Pen and Indian ink over black chalk. Inscribed: *East view of the King's House at Winton. Made by Hiacinthe Bassinet, prisoner of war*, 1762.

EAST VIEW OF THE KING'S HOUSE AT WINTON·MADE BY HIACINTHE BASSINET PRISONER OF WAR·1762·

Fig. 7. HYACINTHE BASSINET: A view of Winchester Palace. Catalogue No. 308

The drawing shows the unfinished palace built by Wren for Charles II and James II. The artist is not otherwise known and was evidently not a professional.

LOUIS BELANGER (1736–1816).

309. View of the Mall with the back entrance to Carlton House.   No. 17167.

208 mm. × 352 mm. Pen, water-colour and gouache. Signed: *Louis Belanger, 1791*.

Made on one of the visits to England of this artist, who exhibited at the Royal Academy of 1790 and 1797. For another drawing of the same view see No. 352.

310. A Cricket Match.   No. 13224.

400 mm. × 553 mm. Gouache. Signed: *Louis Belanger Le romain*, 1798.

FRANÇOIS BOUCHER (1703–1770).

311. Design for the frontispiece to the second volume of Julienne's *Figures de différents Caractères de Paysages et d'Etudes*.   *Pl. 117.* No. 6180.

462 mm. × 296 mm. Black and white chalk on blue paper.

Literature: K. T. Parker, 'The drawings of Antoine Watteau in the British Museum', *Old Master Drawings*, v, 1930, Figure 1.

Mentioned in the eighteenth-century manuscript catalogue as: 'An ornamental sketch'. One of the earliest drawings known by Boucher, executed not later than 1728, the date of the publication of Julienne's second volume.

FRANÇOIS BOUCHER (After).

312. L'Amour Médecin.   No. 13044.

415 mm. × 304 mm. Red chalk. Inscribed in gold: *François Boucher pour l'Amour Medecin de Moliere*. Coll.: N. F. Haym(?); H.R.H. Princess Louise, Duchess of Argyll; H.R.H. The Duke of Kent.

Copy of the engraving by L. Cars after Boucher in the *Œuvres de Molière*, published in 1734 (vol. vii, p. 293).

LOUIS CARROGIS DE CARMONTELLE (1717–1806).

313. M. de Parmentier.   *Pl. 123.* No. 13118.

288 mm. × 183 mm. Black and red chalk, and water-colour. The book beside Parmentier is inscribed: *Commentaire de César*.

Literature: *French Art*, R.A., 1932, p. 143, No. 656.

It is said that the old mount bore the inscription: *M. de Parmentier* 1760. This date would agree with the identification of the sitter as the agriculturalist, Antoine Augustin Parmentier. Carmontelle has here used the pose, and nearly the setting, which appear in his portrait of the Dauphin, son of Louis XV, at Chantilly, also executed in 1760 (cf. F. A. Gruyer, *Les Portraits de Carmontelle*, 1902, p. 2).

314. Mme. Brissard.   *Pl. 122.* No. 13117.

284 mm. × 175 mm. Red and black chalk and water-colour. Inscribed on the eighteenth-century mount: 237.

Literature: *French Art*, R.A., 1932, p. 143, No. 657.

The old mount is said to have been inscribed: *Mme. Brissard*, 1765.

315. Le Comte de Genlis.   No. 13119.

301 mm. × 176 mm. Red and black chalk and water-colour.

Literature: *French Art*, R.A., 1932, p. 144, No. 658.

The old mount is said to have been inscribed: *Le Comte de Genlis*. The sitter was the husband of the authoress,

256 mm. × 185 mm. Black chalk on blue paper.

Inscribed: *L 176* (?) *Sainte Diptare Vierge et martire fille d'un Roy dangleterre*.

Traditionally attributed to Natoire, but certainly earlier. Too feeble for Antoine Coypel, but perhaps a copy after him or by an imitator.

The subject is uncertain. 'Sainte Diptare' is untraceable, but the attributes would fit St. Blida, mother of St. Walstan, or more probably St. Dympna.

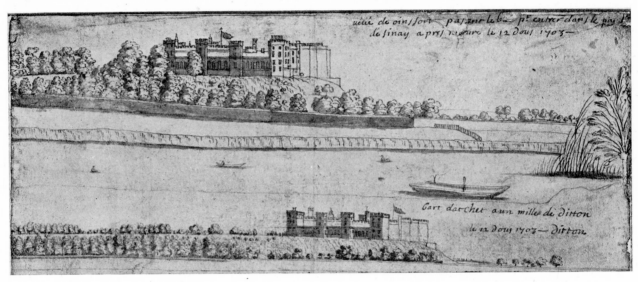

Fig. 8. NOËL(?) GASSELIN: View of Windsor Castle, 1703. Catalogue No. 321

Félicité de Genlis. In pose and setting this drawing is very close to that of the Marquis de Pons at Chantilly (cf. F. A. Gruyer, *Les Portraits de Carmontelle*, 1902, p. 134). In both cases the ages of the sitters point to a date about 1770–1775.

The catalogue of the French Exhibition of 1932 states that these three drawings belonged to Lédans and probably to La Mésangère. The greater part of Carmontelle's works in fact followed this line, and it is quite probable that the present drawings did so. The existence of the number 237 on the margin of the mount to No. 314 confirms that it, at least, formed part of a big series of Carmontelle's drawings which can only have been the collection arranged by Carmontelle, bought by Lédans at his death, and later belonging to La Mésangère. The greater part of this group passed to the Duff Gordon Duff collection, only to return to France *in toto*, when it was bought by the Duc d'Aumale. It is now at Chantilly. It is likely, therefore, that the portrait of Mme. Brissard belonged to Lédans and perhaps to La Mésangère. The fact that the other two drawings have exactly similar eighteenth-century mounts indicates that all three have the same pedigree.

ANTOINE COYPEL (1661–1722). (Manner of.)

316. A Saint.   No. 13120.

JEAN FRANÇOIS DETROY (1679–1752). (After.)

317. Le Rendez-vous à la Fontaine ou L'Alarme.
                                          No. 13116.

348 mm. × 272 mm. Water-colour.

A copy of the painting by Detroy in the South Kensington Museum. Probably executed in the nineteenth century.

FRANÇOIS HUBERT DROUAIS (1727–1775). (Attributed to.)

318. Portrait of the Dauphin, son of Louis XV (?).
                          Pl. 126. No. 13124.

237 mm. × 188 mm. Black and white chalk on blue paper.

This drawing is traditionally identified as Monsieur, later Louis XVIII, but it bears no likeness to other portraits of him. The fact that the sitter is wearing the highest order of the St. Esprit and also the Golden Fleece shows that he must be an important member of the royal family. His features are not unlike those of the Dauphin, eldest son of Louis XV (1729–1765), but such an identification can only be tentative. If it represents him the drawing must date from the last years of his life.

JEAN DUPLESSIS-BERTAUX (1747–1819).

319. Study of a French soldier.   No. 13130.

138 mm. × 84 mm. Black chalk. Signed: *Bertaux*.

320. Study of a French soldier.   No. 13129.

123 mm. × 76 mm. Black chalk.

(1) above, a view of the north front of the castle from the Round Tower to the Curfew Tower.

(2) below, a house in a wood which cannot be identified. These are inscribed: *désinay aprest nature le 19 d ous 1703*. The attribution to Gasselin is based on a series of drawings in the same manner and with the same singular inscriptions at Chatsworth, and on one of the Old

Fig. 9. CHARLES PARROCEL: La Capriole. Catalogue No. 335

Two typical studies of French soldiers, apparently of the period 1795–1805.

GASSELIN (Noël?) (working 1703).

321. *Recto and verso:* A sheet of views of Windsor Castle.
                                        Fig. 8. No. 13242.

163 mm. × 291 mm. Pen and bistre with grey wash over black chalk.

The recto is divided into three long strips each containing a view of the Castle from the north-east. Each is accompanied by an inscription in unusually bad French:

1. *uéué de oinssort passant le b(ac?) pr entrer dans la p(arc?) désinay apres nature le 12 d ous 1703.*

2. *bart datchet a un mille de ditton le 12 d ous 1703—ditton.*

3. *le 13ᵐᵉ d ous 1703—costay qui regarde du costay du part et du bac.*

For the views on the verso the sheet has been turned upright, the lower part being blank. It contains two sketches:

Palace of Marylebone in the possession of the Marylebone Borough Council. The latter is signed: *Gasselin*. The only artist of this name recorded is a Noël Gasselin who was active in Paris in 1677. There is nothing to show whether this is the same as the author of the Windsor drawing.

CLAUDE GILLOT (1673–1722). (Manner of.)

Three scenes from a children's story.

322.   No. 13125.

309 mm. × 379 mm. Black and white chalk with Indian ink wash on blue paper. Inscribed on mount: 1. *Entrée des ambassadeurs de la Princesse: comme quoy cela réveille Monseigneur.*

323.   No. 13126.

308 mm. × 381 mm. Black and white chalk with Indian ink wash on blue paper. Inscribed on mount: 2. *Les Ambassadeurs se prosternant: faut voir l'air gracieux de Monseigneur en les saluant du bonnet.*

324.   No. 13127.

308 mm. × 382 mm. Black and white chalk with Indian ink wash on blue paper. Inscribed on mount: 3. *Harangue des Ambassadeurs. Monseigneur reçoit au milieu des fanfares le portrait et une lettre de la Princesse.*

The inscriptions are in a modern hand but presumably copy those on the old mounts. The story which the drawings illustrate cannot be identified. The drawings are related to certain compositions by Gillot engraved by Caylus, but the handling is too feeble for the artist himself and the technique suggests an imitator working about the middle of the century.

PHILIBERT BENOIT DE LA RUE (c. 1725–1780).

325. A Battle.   *Pl. 120.* No. 13128.

218 mm. × 360 mm. Pen, Indian ink and water-colours. Signed: *Delarue 1756.*

This drawing is clearly by Philibert Benoît de la Rue, the painter of battles and collaborator of Charles Parrocel, rather than by his younger and more classical brother, Louis Félix. A similar drawing in the Louvre (5698) is wrongly attributed to Louis Félix.

JEAN LEGEAY (c. 1715–after 1786).

326. An architectural fantasy.   No. 13143.

285 mm. × 192 mm. Pen and Indian ink. Signed: *Le Geay inven. et fecit.*

The drawing appears to be a design for an engraving. A relief in the foreground contains a caricature head reminiscent of Leonardo's drawings which were popularized in the eighteenth century by the engravings of Caylus and others. A water-colour, also signed by Legeay, with similar classical architecture and grotesque figures, is in the Fitzwilliam Museum, Cambridge.

PIERRE LEGROS THE YOUNGER (1666–1719).

327. Study of a naked man.   No. 4337.

558 mm. × 393 mm. Black chalk heightened with white chalk on buff paper. Inscribed in an eighteenth-century hand: *Le Gros.*

The attribution to Legros, based on the eighteenth-century inscription, is supported by the similarity to other academies by this artist such as Louvre 8647.

JEAN BAPTISTE LE PRINCE (1734–1781).
(Manner of.)

328. A peasant family.   No. 13113.

180 mm. × 133 mm. Water-colour.

329. A tavern scene.   No. 13114.

176 mm. × 130 mm. Water-colour.

Traditionally attributed to Le Prince, but much too weak for him. Probably copies or the work of a poor imitator.

J. LEVERGNE (? – ?).

330. Portrait of Louis XV.   No. 13175.

287 mm. × 218 mm. Pen and Indian ink wash. Signed: *J. Levergne fecit.*

This artist is not otherwise known, but an engraving exists bearing the inscription: *Chez F. Poilly,* which exactly reproduces this drawing except that the head is different, and shows the king as an older man without a hat. The engraving appears to show signs of alteration on the head and it is possible that other copies exist with the head of this drawing. Levergne was probably a hack draughtsman working for Poilly. The age of the king suggests about 1725 as the date for the drawing.

JEAN MICHEL MOREAU THE YOUNGER (1741–1814).

331. Illustration to Ariosto: Melissa and Bradamante before the tomb of Merlin.   No. 13225.

132 mm. × 90 mm. Pen and Indian ink wash. Signed: *J. M. moreau le jeune 1771.* Inscribed on back of mount: *fried^r Geissler a Paris 1806.* Coll.: J. M. F. Geissler, Renouard, Greffuhle. Bought from H. Blairman, Harrogate, 1937.

Literature: Bocher, *Jean-Michel Moreau le Jeune,* 1882, p. 112.

332. Illustration to Ariosto: Roger and Alcina.
                Pl. 127. No. 13226.

132 mm. × 93 mm. Pen and Indian ink wash. Signed: *J. M. moreau le jeune 1770.* Inscribed on back of mount: *friedr Geissler a Paris 1806.* Coll.: J. M. F. Geissler, Renouard, Greffuhle. Bought from H. Blairman, Harrogate, 1937.

Literature: Bocher, *Jean-Michel Moreau le Jeune,* 1882, p. 113.

These two drawings are preparations for engravings in the Italian edition of the *Orlando Furioso* edited by P. and G. Molini and published by Baskerville in 1773. No. 331 is for the plate to Canto III, engraved by N. de Launay (Bocher, *loc. cit.,* No. 278), and No. 332 for the plate to Canto VII, engraved by B. L. Prévost (Bocher, *loc. cit.,* No. 280).

CHARLES PARROCEL (1688–1752).

Sketches for plates in the *Ecole de Cavalerie* by La Guérinière, Paris 1733.

333. Le Terre-à-terre.   No. 13131.

135 mm. × 141 mm. Pen and bistre. Inscribed: *5.*

Study for plate opposite p. 78, engraved by N. Tardieu, with background added. This drawing and No. 334 belong to the 'Alures artificielles: Airs près de terre'.

334. Le Pas. No. 13132.

131 mm. × 142 mm. Pen and bistre. Inscribed: *Alures*. Study for plate opposite p. 74, engraved by J. Audran, but with background added.

335. La Capriole. *Fig. 9.* No. 13133.

105 mm. × 168 mm. Pen and bistre. Inscribed: *11*. Study for plate opposite p. 81, engraved by J. Audran. The engraving also contains other figures and background. This drawing and No. 336 belong to the 'Alures artificielles: Airs relevez'.

336. L'Epaule en dedans. No. 13134.

232 mm. × 200 mm. Pen and bistre on buff paper. Inscribed: *12*. Study for plate opposite p. 104, engraved by N. Tardieu. The engraving has a landscape background and includes the figure of a man leaning on a stick, whose hand is just visible on the extreme right of the drawing.

337. Le Marquis de Beauvilliers. *Pl. 118.* No. 13135.

228 mm. × 213 mm. Pen and bistre on buff paper. Inscribed: *13*. Study for plate opposite p. 109, engraved by N. Dupuis. The engraving has a background of which one part, a wall, is indicated in the drawing.

338. Monsieur de Kraut. No. 13136.

228 mm. × 232 mm. Pen and bistre on buff paper. Inscribed: *14*. Study for plate opposite p. 114, engraved by L. Cars. The engraving has a more elaborate background which includes, however, the two posts seen in the drawing.

339. Charles, Prince de Nassau. No. 13137.

227 mm. × 201 mm. Pen and bistre.

Study for plate opposite p. 143, engraved by L. Desplaces, with the addition of a landscape background.

Nos. 336–338 are all on the same paper and appear to form part of a single sheet showing a series of steps, which were probably named in the scroll, of which parts can be seen in the drawings. All seven drawings are irregularly cut probably from much larger sheets.

In the engravings Nos. 337–339 are transformed into portraits, but there is no indication of this intention in the drawings, which appear to be pure studies of paces. Paintings by Parrocel based on Nos. 336–339 are also at Windsor.

340. Studies of Soldier's heads. *Pl. 119.* No. 13138.

146 mm. × 231 mm. Black and red chalk on buff paper. Inscribed: *grenadiers (?) C. Parrocel*.

A comparison of the headdress with the plate of Eisen's *Nouveau Recueil des Troupes qui Forment la Garde et Maison du Roy*, 1756, confirms the doubtful inscription and shows that these are in fact Grenadiers.

341. Studies of Soldiers' heads. No. 13139.

143 mm. × 232 mm. Black and red chalk on buff paper. Inscribed: *cavaller C. Parrocel*.

A pair to No. 340. The exact cavalry regiment to which these troopers belong cannot be identified.

BERNARD PICART (1673–1733).

342. Isaac blessing Jacob. No. 6177.

300 mm. × 415 mm. Red chalk, partly drawn over in pen and Indian ink. Inscribed in an eighteenth-century hand: *E. le Sueur ft*.

This drawing is mentioned in the manuscript catalogue among those attributed to Le Sueur, but it is described as 'doubtful'. It is, however, an exact study, in reverse, for an engraving inscribed: *Bernard Picart Invent. à Paris chez Cars*, and is therefore presumably by Picart.

343. A lady resting. *Pl. 115.* No. 13103.

231 mm. × 185 mm. Two different red chalks.

This drawing is traditionally attributed to C. N. Cochin, but the costume shows that it cannot be later than the first decade of the eighteenth century. The attribution to Picart, suggested by Dr. K. T. Parker, is based on the close resemblance to a signed and engraved drawing of 1708 in the Ashmolean (cf. K. T. Parker, *Catalogue of the Collection of Drawings in the Ashmolean Museum*, 1938, i, p. 263, No. 544), and on an engraving signed: *B. Picart fe. et ex.* and dated 1703, which shows the head and shoulders of the lady in the drawing, but reversed. (For an undated impression, cf. M. Leloir, *Histoire du Costume*, x, pl. 34.) The drawing is, therefore, to be dated 1703 or slightly earlier.

344. Studies of women's heads. No. 13106.

83 mm. × 121 mm. Pen and Indian ink wash.

345. Studies of men's heads. No. 13105.

123 mm. × 84 mm. Pen and Indian ink wash.

These two drawings depict fashions in headdress and wigs of the first decade of the eighteenth century. The attribution to Picart is based on the resemblance to his fashion drawings in general and to the engravings mentioned under the last drawing (No. 343) in particular. As far as can be ascertained at present no engravings exist exactly reproducing these drawings, but several of the women's heads in No. 344 and the middle head on the left-hand side of No. 345 reappear in slightly different form in engravings by Picart reproduced by M. Leloir, *Histoire du Costume*, x, pl. 34.

No. 345 is purely a fashion plate, whereas in No. 344 each study is accompanied by a small drawing in outline showing the head without the cap, or the head and cap reduced to their simplest terms. It is likely, therefore, that this drawing was intended to illustrate some handbook giving instructions for drawing the human figure in contemporary costume.

Four love-scenes.

346. 71 mm. × 105 mm. Water-colour with gold. No. 13108.

347. 73 mm. × 105 mm. Water-colour with gold. No. 13109.

348. 74 mm. × 107 mm. Water-colour with gold. No. 13110.

349. 75 mm. × 107 mm. Water-colour with gold. No. 13111.

These water-colours are rather gayer than Picart's usual work, and are very strong in colour. Each drawing shows a pair of lovers in a landscape. The dress indicates a date about 1700–1710. For a very similar composition engraved in colour by Picart cf. Leloir, *Histoire du Costume*, x, pl. 33.

JEAN LOUIS PRIEUR (1759–1795).

350. Study of two soldiers and a condemned man.
Fig. 10. No. 13140.

137 mm. × 163 mm. Black chalk. An inscription in a late eighteenth-century or early nineteenth century hand is now on the back of the mount: *Dernier dessin de Prieur, fameux Jacobin, membre et Juré du tribunal révolutionnaire, guillotiné avec fouquier tinville le 18 floréal l'an 3e de la république. Ce dessin représente une des victimes dont il jugeoit 60 à mort, par jour. ce cannibal se plaisoit a dessiner la figure de ceux qu'il envoyoit à l'Echafaux.*

Prieur was an active participant in the French Revolution and with another artist, Claude Louis Châtelet, was a close friend of Fouquier-Tinville. All three played a leading part on the Tribunal Révolutionnaire and were tried and executed together on 6th May 1795. At the trial Prieur was accused of making 'caricatures' of those whom he condemned to death (cf. Nolhac, 'Les Dessins de Jean Louis Prieur', *Revue de l'Art*, x, 1901, p. 319), a fact to which reference is made in the inscription accompanying this drawing. The inscription actually states

Fig. 10. J. L. PRIEUR: Two soldiers and a condemned man. Catalogue No. 350

that the drawing is one of those made in this way, but this is rather doubtful, since it cannot properly be described as a 'caricature', and further, the only figure which could possibly be identified as the condemned man is one which appears in a very minor position on the extreme right. It may, however, well be a sketch made during the proceedings of the tribunal. According to the inscription it is his last work, and therefore probably dates from 1795.

The only other known drawings by Prieur seem to be the series in the Louvre for the *Tableaux de la Révolution Française (1789–1792)* (published by Nolhac, *Tableaux de Paris pendant la Révolution française, 64 Dessins de J. L. Prieur*, 1902). These are all of large compositions with many figures and afford no basis for direct stylistic comparison, but many of them have a similar use of rather mechanical hatching, and there is no reason to question the attribution of the Windsor drawing to him.

HYACINTHE RIGAUD (1659–1743). (After.)

351. Portrait of Louis XV as a child. No. 13070.

427 mm. × 326 mm. Black, red and white chalk on buff paper.

A studio copy of a portrait of which the bust was engraved by N. Larmessin the younger in 1720. The original may be the painting at Versailles (Soulié, i, p. 44, No. 170).

JOHN ROULLIER (? – ?).

352. View of the Mall with the back entrance to Carlton House. No. 17166.

284 mm. × 379 mm. Black chalk and water-colour. Inscribed on mount: *a view in St. James's Parc John Rouiller del. 1788 Camberwell.*

This artist is not otherwise recorded and it is not even certain that he was French. His surname and the French spelling *Parc* in the inscription point in this direction whereas his Christian name *John* suggests that he may have been English. The drawing is included here, however, partly because of the close parallel which it provides with No. 309.

ELISABETH LOUISE VIGEE-LEBRUN (1755–1842).

353. Portrait of Monsieur, Comte de Provence, later Louis XVIII (1755–1824). *Pl. 125.* No. 13122.

376 mm. × 290 mm. Oval. Black and white chalk on buff paper, touched with Indian ink wash. Inscribed: *Monsieur—Le Brun 1777 ft* (?).

354. Portrait of Madame, Comtesse de Provence.
Pl. 124. No. 13123.

384 mm. × 289 mm. Oval. Black, white and red chalk. Inscribed: *Madame. P Mme Le Brun 1777.*

These portraits were engraved in mezzotint as a pair by W. Pether in 1778. The drawings both have indications at the bottom of the shortening of the oval, which is followed by the engraver. The inscriptions on the mezzotint read: *Mme Le Brun pinx*, but no painted versions are known.

The Comtesse de Provence was Louise Marie Joséphine, daughter of the Duke of Savoy (1753–1810).

ANTOINE WATTEAU (1684–1721).

355. Head of a man in a turban. *Pl. 116.* No. 3948.

214 mm. × 158 mm. Black and red chalks heightened with body-colour.

Hitherto among the drawings by Castiglione from a volume belonging to Consul Smith. The drawing is, however, evidently French, and the attribution to Watteau is confirmed without hesitation by Dr. K. T. Parker, who believes it to be an early work. It is not connected with any painting by the artist.

ANTOINE WATTEAU (School of).

356. Studies of hands holding swords and pikes.
Military Costumes, v, p. 4v.

132 mm. × 189 mm. Irregularly cut. Red chalk.

356a. Study of Trees. No. 5814.

203 mm. × 320 mm. Red chalk.

Traditionally classified among the Italian drawings, but probably by an imitator of Watteau.

ANONYMOUS ARTIST (c. 1730–1740).

357. Design for a staircase. No. 13043.

443 mm. × 301 mm. Pen and grey wash.

A rather mechanical drawing by an architect working in the French Rococo style. Perhaps by a pupil of Boffrand.

ANONYMOUS ARTIST (c. 1750).

358. A Chinese room. No. 17184.

171 mm. × 303 mm. Pen, Indian ink and water-colour. Inscribed: *Salon a la Chinoise.*

A genuine attempt to reproduce a Chinese room, and not an occidental Chinoiserie.

ANONYMOUS ARTIST (c. 1750–1770).

359. Love scene. No. 13115.

140 mm. × 172 mm. Water-colour.

Part of a fan-design, cut down and patched. Traditionally ascribed to J. B. Le Prince, with whose style it has no connection. An inferior *pastiche* of the manner current among the less good followers of Boucher.

ANONYMOUS ARTIST (c. 1770).

360. The terrace of an Italian villa. No. 6130.

263 mm. × 415 mm. Black chalk heightened with white on buff paper.

361. Italian landscape. No. 6152.

240 mm. × 403 mm. Black chalk and Indian ink wash heightened with white.

Two drawings of poor quality, apparently by the same hand. Probably by a minor contemporary of Hubert Robert working in Italy.

ANONYMOUS ARTIST (c. 1780).

362. Tomb of a French Nobleman. No. 17183.

247 mm. × 207 mm. Pen, Indian ink and water-colour.

A medallion with a bust, below which hangs the order of St. Esprit. A tablet for the inscription supports the medallion, beside which are two lamps.

ANONYMOUS ARTIST (c. 1780).

363. Street Scene. *Pl. 121.* No. 13112.

234 mm. × 347 mm. Pen, Indian ink and water-colour. Inscribed in lower right-hand corner: *La rad . . . . .* Inscribed on mount: *La Rue.*

The inscription on the mount could refer either to the subject of the drawing or to the artist's name. But since the style has no connection with that of either Louis Félix or Philbert Benoît de La Rue, the only artists of that name working in the later eighteenth century, it seems likely that it is a description of the scene.

The drawing shows an animated street, with classical and Gothic buildings, and a neo-classical fountain. In the foreground a troupe of Italian comedians are giving a performance. The inscription on the drawing itself cannot be deciphered, and was probably only meant to be a scribble except for the first few letters.

ANONYMOUS ARTIST (*temp.* Louis XV).

In *Military Costumes*, iv (pp. 25–26v) is a series of water-colours representing French uniforms in the reign of Louis XV.

Fig. 11. A. J. B. BAYOT and A. DAUZATS: The entry of Queen Victoria into Paris. Catalogue No. 366

NINETEENTH CENTURY

The nineteenth-century drawings and water-colours fall into three main classes, viz:

    I. Souvenir Drawings contained in *Souvenir Album*, iv, and consisting of:

      (a) A series presented to Queen Victoria after the Royal visit to King Louis Philippe at Château d'Eu in 1843, and mentioned in Queen Victoria's Diary under date October 8th 1844. (Referred to as *Louis Philippe Souvenir*.)

      (b) Ten drawings presented by Napoleon III after the Royal Visit of 1855 and mentioned in the same Diary on December 25th, 1855. (Referred to as *Napoleon III 1855 Souvenir*.)

      (c) A series presented by the City of Paris in commemoration of the Fêtes at the Hôtel de Ville on the same occasion.

      (d) A series commissioned by Queen Victoria after the same visit.

    II. A large number of drawings of the uniforms etc. of the Allies in 1815, contained in the collection of Military Costumes.

    III. Miscellaneous drawings and portraits mounted in the general collection and deriving from various sources, the principal of which is an album bearing the name of the Prince de Joinville.

FRANÇOIS BERNARD BARRY (1813–1905).

364. The Royal Visit to King Louis Philippe, 1843. The Victoria and Albert arriving off Le Tréport at 5 p.m. September 2nd. *Souvenir*, iv, p. 1 (a).

215 mm. × 445 mm. Water-colour. Signed: *Fçois Barry*. Louis Philippe Souvenir. The artist exhibited a picture of this subject in the Salon of 1845.

ANTOINE LOUIS BARYE (1796–1875).

365. Two tigers. No. 13189.

246 mm. × 330 mm. Water-colour. Signed: *Barye*. Coll.: de Joinville.

ADOLPHE JEAN BAPTISTE BAYOT (1810–?) and ADRIEN DAUZATS (1804–1868).

366. The Royal Visit to the Emperor Napoleon III, 1855. Entry of Queen Victoria into Paris, August 18th. *Fig. 11. Souvenir*, iv, p. 40 (a).

325 mm. × 475 mm. Water-colour. Inscribed: *Bayot et Dauzats*. Commissioned 1855, price not stated. Reprod.: R. Davies, pl. xvii (b).

The Royal cortège is shown passing the Porte St. Denis.

JOSEPH LOUIS HIPPOLYTE BELLANGE (1800–1866).

367. The Grandfather. No. 13190.

235 mm. × 190 mm. Water-colour. Signed: *Hte. Bellangé 1829*. Coll.: de Joinville.

368. The Royal visit to King Louis Philippe, 1843. Review of the 1st Regiment of Carabiniers, Tuesday, September 5th. *Souvenir*, iv, p. 15.

335 mm. × 491 mm. Water-colour. Signed: *Hte Bellangé*. Louis Philippe Souvenir.

The Prince Consort, accompanied by the Prince de Joinville, the Duc d'Aumale and the Duc de Montpensier, takes the salute.

369. The Royal Visit to the Emperor Napoleon III, 1855. The Imperial Hunt at the Château de la Muette in the forest of St. Germain, August 25th. *Souvenir*, iv, p. 56.

326 mm. × 472 mm. Water-colour. Signed: *Hte Bellangé*, 1855. Commissioned 1855 (1,500 fr.). Reprod.: R. Davies, pl. xix (b).

JEAN JOSEPH FRANÇOIS BELLEL (1816–1898).

370. Woodland landscape. No. 13192.

140 mm. × 260 mm. Brown wash, grey-blue in sky. Signed: *J. Bellel*. Coll.: de Joinville.

371. Woodland scene. No. 13191.

235 mm. × 180 mm. Oval. Brown wash and white, grey-blue in sky. Signed: *J. Bellel*. Coll.: de Joinville.

C. R. DE BERENGER.

Four water-colours of English Uniforms with this name and dated 1812 and 1813 are in *Military Costumes*, iv, pp. 49–52. Nos. 16401–4. The artist appears to be unrecorded.

MAX BERTHELIN (1811–1877).

372. The Royal Visit to the Emperor Napoleon III, 1855. Illuminations at the Hôtel de Ville, Paris, 23rd August. *Souvenir*, iv, p. 47 (b).

315 mm. × 458 mm. Water-colour. Signed: *1855 Max Berthelin*.

MAX BERTHELIN and JULES WORMS (1832–?).

373. The Royal Visit to the Emperor Napoleon III, 1855. The Hôtel de Ville, Paris, August, 1855. Galerie des Fêtes. *Souvenir*, iv, p. 50 (c).

283 mm. × 436 mm. Water-colour. Signed: *Max Berthelin 1855*. Inscribed: *Figures par Worms*.

Dussieux, *Les Artistes français à l'Etranger*, Third Ed., 1876, p. 295, credits Berthelin wrongly with all the

F

drawings, executed under the supervision of the architect Baltard, for the Souvenir of the Fêtes at the Hôtel de Ville presented by the City of Paris to Queen Victoria.

LOUIS NAPOLEON BONAPARTE. (Attributed to).

374. A Grenadier. No. 13229.

143 mm. × 92 mm. Pen and wash on brown paper. Inscribed: *Louis Napoléon Bonaparte 1833* (apparently not a signature).

ROSA MARIE ROSALIE BONHEUR (1822–1899).

375. A pony. No. 13236.

157 mm. × 247 mm. Pencil on brown paper. Signed: *Rosa Bonheur.*

376. A donkey. No. 13237.

225 mm. × 281 mm. Water-colour. Signed: *Rosa Bonheur.*

LEON JOSEPH FLORENTIN BONNAT (1834–1922).

377. A youthful figure raising a torch and kneeling on the back of a winged Pegasus. No. 13233.

280 mm. × 214 mm. Pen, blue and pink wash on card. Signed: *Ln. Bonnat 1896.*

WILLIAM ADOLPHE BOUGUEREAU (1825–1905).

378. Italian peasant woman with a child in her arms. No. 13235.

280 mm. × 214 mm. Pen on card. Signed: *Wm. Bouguereau 1897.*

CHARLES MARIE BOUTON (1781–1853).

379. A courtyard. No. 13193.

97 mm. × 143 mm. Brown and green gouache. Signed: *Bouton.* Coll.: de Joinville.

CHARLES EMILE AUGUSTE DURAND, called CAROLUS-DURAN (1837–1913).

380. Portrait of lady. No. 13234.

245 mm. × 177 mm. Water-colour on card. Signed: *Carolus Duran 1896.*

NICOLAS TOUSSAINT CHARLET (1792–1845).

381. An old peasant. No. 13195.

257 mm. × 181 mm. Water-colour on brown paper. Signed: *Charlet.* Coll.: de Joinville.

382. Peasant scene. No. 13194.

188 mm. × 161 mm. Pencil with touches of colour on brown paper. Signed: *Charlet.* Coll.: de Joinville.

There are also five water-colours of costumes by this artist in *Military Costumes*, ix, pp. 71, 72.

VICTOR JOSEPH CHAVET (1822–1906).

383. The Royal Visit to the Emperor Napoleon III, 1855. Ball in the Galerie des Glaces, Versailles, 25th August. *Souvenir*, iv, p. 57 (a).

298 mm. × 490 mm. Water-colour. Signed: *V. Chavet.* Napoleon III 1855 Souvenir. Literature: Dussieux, 1876, p. 295. Reprod.: R. Davies, pl. xx (b).

384. The same. Queen Victoria and the Prince Consort with the Emperor and Empress in the Galerie des Glaces, Versailles. *Souvenir*, iv, p. 57 (b).

315 mm. × 485 mm. Water-colour. Signed: *V. Chavet.* Napoleon III 1855 Souvenir. Literature: Dussieux, 1876, p. 295.

JULES LOUIS PHILIPPE COIGNET (1798–1860).

385. A ruined cottage. No. 13196.

249 mm. × 197 mm. Water-colour. Signed: *J. Coignet.* Coll.: de Joinville.

JEAN JOSEPH BENJAMIN CONSTANT (1845–1902).

386. The head of an Arab. No. 13238.

197 mm. × 165 mm. Pen. Signed: *Benjamin Constant* 1897.

ERNEST GEORGES COQUARD (or COQUART) (1831–1902).

387. The Royal Visit to the Emperor Napoleon III, 1855. The Hôtel de Ville, Paris, fountain under the staircase of honour. *Souvenir*, iv, p. 48 (a).

277 mm. × 203 mm. Water-colour. Signed: *Coquard.*

388. The same. The Hôtel de Ville, Paris, one of the two grand staircases. *Souvenir*, iv, p. 49.

401 mm. × 310 mm. Water-colour. Signed: *E. Coquard.*

ADOLPHE JEAN FRANÇOIS MARIN DALLEMAGNE (1811–after 1878).

389. The Royal Visit to the Emperor Napoleon III, 1855. View from the ground floor of Queen Victoria's apartments at St. Cloud. *Souvenir*, iv, p. 44 (a).

320 mm. × 470 mm. Water-colour. Signed: *Adolphe Dallemagne.* Commissioned 1855 (800 fr.).

ADRIEN DAUZATS (1804–1868).

390. Cordova. No. 13197.

217 mm. × 293 mm. Water-colour. Signed: *A. Dauzats, Cordoue.* Coll.: de Joinville.

391. An Arabian Youth. No. 13198.

425 mm. × 295 mm. Water-colour. Signed: *A. Dauzats 1834.* Coll.: de Joinville.

392. Two Arabs. No. 13199.

465 mm. × 367 mm. Water-colour. Signed: *A. Dauzats 1833*. Coll.: de Joinville.

393. The Royal Visit to King Louis Philippe, 1843. Queen Victoria's Drawing Room at Château d'Eu. *Souvenir*, iv, p. 6 (*a*).

185 mm. × 346 mm. Water-colour. Signed: *A. Dauzats*. Louis Philippe Souvenir. Reprod.: R. Davies, pl. v (*a*).

394. The same. Queen Victoria's bedroom at Château d'Eu. *Souvenir*, iv, p. 6 (*b*).

234 mm. × 362 mm. Water-colour. Signed: *A. Dauzats*. Louis Philippe Souvenir.

395. The same. The Church of St. Laurent at Eu with the Royal Party visiting. *Souvenir*, iv, p. 17 (*b*).

381 mm. × 302 mm. Water-colour. Signed: *A. Dauzats 1844*. Louis Philippe Souvenir.

See also No. 366.

LOUIS DAVID.

A nineteenth-century water-colour signed: *David (Louis)*, in *Military Costumes*, v, p. 62, showing a cuirassier of 1793 in combat, may be by Jean Louis David (1792–1868) who exhibited water-colours from 1833 to 1866, or by Baron Jacques Louis Jules David (1829–1886), painter and etcher, and grandson and biographer of the celebrated Louis David.

ALEXANDRE GABRIEL DECAMPS (1803–1860).

396. The Showman. No. 13200.

230 mm. × 158 mm. Water-colour. Signed: *D.C.* Exhibited: Burlington Fine Arts Club, 1937, No. 161. Coll.: de Joinville.

397. Duck Shooting. No. 13201.

165 mm. × 222 mm. Water-colour. Signed: *Decamps*. Coll.: de Joinville.

398. Poste Turc. No. 13202.

324 mm. × 242 mm. Water-colour. Signed: *Decamps*. *Poste Turc* written at head. Coll.: de Joinville.

JEAN BAPTISTE EDOUARD DETAILLE (1848–1912).

399. A Life Guard, mounted. No. 13158.

209 mm. × 258 mm. Pen on brown paper. Signed: *Edouard Detaille, 7 Mars 1878*. Hôtel du Figaro.

400. Napoleon III and a Zouave. No. 13159.

218 mm. × 167 mm. Pen and grey wash. Signed: *Edouard Detaille 1907*.

401. The Emperor Napoleon I. No. 13239.

233 mm. × 183 mm. Pencil and water-colour on brown paper. Signed: *Edouard Detaille 1907*.

402. The Uhlan's Progress. No. 13240.

220 mm. × 174 mm. Pen and grey wash. Signed: *Edouard Detaille*.

There are also eight water-colours of English uniforms by this artist in *Military Costumes*, xi, and one in xii, p. 45.

JULES PIERRE MICHEL DIETERLE.
See No. 479.

ARTHUR DIETS (working 1855) & JULES WORMS.

403. The Royal Visit to the Emperor Napoleon III. 1855. The Hôtel de Ville, Paris, the Council Chamber. *Souvenir*, iv, p. 54 (*b*).

297 mm. × 397 mm. Water-colour. Signed: *Arthur Diets 1853*. Inscribed: *Les figures par Worms*.

404. The same. The Hôtel de Ville, Paris, entrance to the Galerie des Glaces. *Souvenir*, iv, p. 52 (*d*).

270 mm. × 198 mm. Water-colour. Signed: *Arthur Diets*. Inscribed: *Les figures par Worms*.

Diets appears to be unrecorded.

GODEFROY DURAND (1832– ?).

405. The Funeral of the Prince Imperial at Camden House, Chislehurst, 1879. The arrival of the Remains at 9 p.m., July 11th. *Souvenir*, iv, p. 65 (*a*).

193 mm. × 325 mm. Pen and ink wash. Signed: *Godefroy Durand 11 juillet 1879, 9 heures du soir*.

406. The same. The Pall Bearers. *Souvenir*, iv, p. 66 (*a*).

198 mm. × 292 mm. Pen and ink wash. Signed: *Godefroy Durand 1879*.

The pall bearers were the Prince of Wales, the Duke of Edinburgh, the Duke of Cambridge and the Crown Prince of Sweden and Norway.

407. The same. The Chapelle Ardente, July 12th. *Souvenir*, iv, p. 65 (*b*).

300 mm. × 270 mm. Pen and slight wash. Signed: *Godefroy Durand 1879*.

408. The same. The Burial, July 12th. *Souvenir*, iv, p. 66 (*b*).

317 mm. × 517 mm. Pen and ink wash. Signed: *Godefroy Durand 1879*.

Further drawings by this draughtsman are in *Military Costumes*, iv, p. 94 ff.

ESCRIBE.

Water-colours with this name and dated 1889 are in *Military Costumes*, xii, pp. 48 and 50. The artist appears to be unrecorded.

EUGENE (LAMI).

Twenty-six water-colours of French uniforms, mostly signed: *Eugène 1817 Paris*, accepted by Lemoisne (1912, p. 6, and 1914, p. 363, etc.) as by Lami are in *Military Costumes*, iv.

FESTEAU.

409. The Royal Visit to the Emperor Napoleon III, 1855. The Hôtel de Ville, Paris, Salle des Cariatides.
Souvenir, iv, p. 51 (*c*).

397 mm. × 297 mm. Water-colour. Signed: *Festeau 1855.* The artist appears to be unrecorded.

NOEL DIEUDONNE FINART (1792–1852).

Military Costumes, ix, consists almost entirely of water-colours of uniforms and portraits of the Allied forces by this artist. A similar water-colour by him is in vol. iv, p. 14.

SIMEON JEAN ANTOINE FORT (1793–1861).

410. The Royal Visit to King Louis Philippe, 1843. The drive to Monthuon through Le Tréport, Sunday, Sept. 3rd.   *Souvenir*, iv, p. 12 (*a*).

280 mm. × 400 mm. Water-colour. Signed: *Siméon Fort.* Louis Philippe Souvenir.

411. The same. The return through the park of the Château d'Eu, Sunday, Sept. 3rd. *Souvenir*, iv, p. 12 (*b*).

300 mm. × 462 mm. Water-colour. Signed: *Siméon Fort.* Louis Philippe Souvenir.

412. The same. Luncheon at the Mont d'Orléans, Forest of Eu, Sept. 4th.   *Souvenir*, iv, p. 14 (*a*).

303 mm. × 434 mm. Water-colour. Signed: *Siméon Fort 1843.* Louis Philippe Souvenir.

413. The same. Changing horses at the Arbre des Princes, Forest of Eu, Tuesday, Sept. 5th. *Souvenir*, iv, p. 19 (*a*).

290 mm. × 238 mm. Water-colour. Signed: *Siméon Fort 1843.* Louis Philippe Souvenir. Reprod.: R. Davies, pl. v (*b*). Subject exhibited at the Salon 1845.

414. The same. Open air luncheon at Ste. Catherine-à-Garde-Chasse, Forest of Eu, Sept. 6th.
Souvenir, iv, p. 19 (*b*).

293 mm. × 405 mm. Water-colour. Signed: *Siméon Fort 1843.* Louis Philippe Souvenir.

An almost identical representation was engraved by Joseph Skelton for his *Historical Illustrations of the Château*

d'*Eu*, London, 1844, after Karl Girardet, who exhibited at the Salon of 1845 a picture of this subject which was acquired by King Louis Philippe.

SIMEON JEAN ANTOINE FORT and FRANZ XAVIER WINTERHALTER (1806–1873).

415. The same. The Montpensier summer house at Château d'Eu, Sunday, Sept. 3rd, 7.30 a.m.
Souvenir, iv, p. 10 (*a*).

272 mm. × 237 mm. Water-colour. Louis Philippe Souvenir.

416. The same. In the Queen's sitting-room, Château d'Eu.   *Souvenir*, iv, p. 13 (*a*).

282 mm. × 234 mm. Water-colour. Louis Philippe Souvenir.

The two Queens and (?) the Duchesse de Nemours seated in arm-chairs, conversing.

ELISABETH FORT-SIMEON (*née* Collin) (working 1835–1865).

417. Landscape with winding river.   No. 13203.

195 mm. × 265 mm. Water-colour. Coll.: de Joinville.

CHARLES FOUQUERAY (1869– ?).

A water-colour signed *Fouqueray* 1914 in *Military Costumes*, xii, p. 45, is presumably by the sea painter and illustrator Charles Fouqueray.

JEAN BAPTISTE FORTUNE DE FOURNIER (1798–1864).

418. The Royal Visit to the Emperor Napoleon III, 1855. Queen Victoria's dressing room, St. Cloud.
Souvenir, iv, p. 42 (*a*).

328 mm. × 475 mm. Water-colour. Signed: *F. de Fournier 1855.* Commissioned 1855 (800 fr.).

Her Majesty writing at a small table.

419. The same. Queen Victoria's drawing-room at St. Cloud.   *Souvenir*, iv, p. 42 (*b*).

328 mm. × 472 mm. Water-colour. Signed: *F. de Fournier 1855 à Paris.* Commissioned 1855, price not stated.

Her Majesty seated looking at a coloured portrait of the Emperor in a book. The Prince Consort deep in another armchair reading a newspaper, barely visible.

FRANÇOIS LOUIS FRANÇAIS (1814–1897).

420. The Royal Visit to the Emperor Napoleon III, 1855. The Bois de Boulogne, the Lake and the Moorish Pavilion.   *Souvenir*, iv., p. 44 (*b*).

327 mm. × 472 mm. Water-colour. Signed: *Français 1855.* Commissioned 1855 (1,000 fr.).

ALEXANDRE THOMAS FRANCIA (1815 or 1820–1884).

421. Queen Victoria's Visit to the King of the Belgians at Laeken, 1843. The Royal Yacht entering Ostend, September 19th.   *Souvenir*, iv, p. 27 (*b*).

280 mm. × 434 mm. Water-colour. Signed: *A. T. Francia* (A.T.F. in monogram).

JEAN LOUIS CHARLES GARNIER (1825–1898) and JULES WORMS.

422. The Royal Visit to the Emperor Napoleon III, 1855. The Hôtel de Ville, Paris, Galerie des Paysages du Département.   *Souvenir*, iv, p. 52 (*c*).

269 mm. × 200 mm. Water-colour. Signed: *C. Garnier* (in pencil) and *Garnier* (in ink). Inscribed: *Figures par Worms* (in pencil).

423. The same. The Hôtel de Ville, Paris, the Throne Room.   *Souvenir*, iv, p. 54 (*a*).

302 mm. × 399 mm. Water-colour. Signed: *C. Garnier 1855*. Inscribed: *Worms*.

Presumably by the well-known architect of the Opera House at Paris.

CHARLES GEOFFREY-DECHAUNE (living artist).

The *Windsor Topographical Volume* contains eight water-colours, views of Windsor Castle and Eton, 1911.

JEAN LOUIS ANDRE THEODORE GERICAULT (1791–1824).

424. *Recto:* A horse in a stable.   No. 13204.

201 mm. × 260 mm. Pencil and brown wash on brownish paper.

Verso: A carthorse.

Pencil and sepia wash. Inscribed: *(Géri)cault*. Coll.: de Joinville.

PIERRE GIRARD (1806–1872).

425. Landscape on the banks of the Seine.   No. 13205.

230 mm. × 307 mm. Water-colour. Signed: *Girard 1833*. Coll.: de Joinville.

KARL GIRARDET (1813–1871).

426. The Royal Visit to King Louis Philippe, 1843. Queen Victoria taking the Salute of the Garde Nationale from the Balcony at the Château d'Eu, Sept. 2nd, 7 p.m.
                                Souvenir, iv, p. 5.

357 mm. × 306 mm. Water-colour. Signed: *Karl Girardet 1844*. Louis Philippe Souvenir.

427. The Royal Visit to the Emperor Napoleon III, 1855. Queen Victoria arriving at the Maison du Seigneur, Petit Trianon, Aug. 20th.   *Souvenir*, iv, p. 45 (*b*).

322 mm. × 470 mm. Water-colour. Signed: *Karl Girardet 1855*. Commissioned 1855 (800 fr.).

PIERRE EUGENE GRANDSIRE (1825–1905).

428. The Royal Visit to the Emperor Napoleon III, 1855. St. Cloud from the 'Horse-shoe'.
                                Souvenir, iv, p. 41 (*b*).

318 mm. × 465 mm. Water-colour. Signed: *E. Grandsire*. Commissioned 1855, price not stated. Reprod.: R. Davies, pl. xix (*a*).

JEAN ANTOINE THEODORE GUDIN (1802–1880).

429. A wreck on the coast off Brest.   No. 13206.

182 mm. × 291 mm. Sepia. Signed: *T. Gudin, 1ᵉʳ Jᵉʳ 1836*. Coll.: de Joinville.

EUGENE CHARLES FRANÇOIS GUERARD (1821–1866).

430. The Royal Visit to the Emperor Napoleon III, 1855. The Entry of Queen Victoria into Paris, Aug. 18th.   *Souvenir*, iv, p. 40 (*b*).

340 mm. × 497 mm. Water-colour. Signed: *1855, E. Guérard*. Napoleon III 1855 Souvenir. Reprod.: R. Davies, pl. xviii (*a*).

The Royal Cortège passing under a triumphal arch.

431. The same. Departure of Queen Victoria and the Prince Consort from Paris, Aug. 27th.
                                Souvenir, iv, p. 60.

338 mm. × 518 mm. Water-colour. Signed: *E. Guérard 1855*. Napoleon III 1855 Souvenir.

The Royal Cortège arriving at the decorated Gare de Strasbourg.

These two drawings are wrongly given by Dussieux, *op. cit.*, p. 295, to Amédée Guérard.

JEAN BAPTISTE LOUIS HUBERT (1801–after 1869).

432. Landscape with ruined castle.   No. 13207.

209 mm. × 276 mm. Water-colour. Signed: *Hubert*. Coll.: de Joinville.

433. Open landscape.   No. 13208.

130 mm. × 219 mm. Water-colour. Signed: *Hubert*. Coll.: de Joinville.

CHARLES GUSTAVE HUILLARD (1825–1893) and JULES WORMS.

434. The Royal Visit to the Emperor Napoleon III, 1855. The Hôtel de Ville, Paris, Gallery and fountain in the Salon des Prévôts.   *Souvenir*, iv, p. 50 (*b*).

270 mm. × 198 mm. Water-colour. Signed: *G. Huillard*. Inscribed: *Figures par Worms*.

Fig. 12. P. E. LACOSTE: Préfecture de Police. Catalogue No. 454

Fig. 13. E. LAMI: The arrival of Queen Victoria at Le Tréport. Catalogue No. 461

435. The same. The Hôtel de Ville, Paris, one of the fountains in the Salle des Cariatides.

Souvenir, iv, p. 51 (a).

283 mm. × 197 mm. Water-colour. Signed: *G. Huillard.* Inscribed: *Figures par Worms.*

EUGENE HUOT (Exhibited 1836–1841).

436. A procession to the Abbey of St. Denis. No. 13155.

321 mm. × 460 mm. Water-colour. Signed: *E. Huot, 1840.*

LOUIS GABRIEL EUGENE ISABEY (1803–1886).

437. Coast scene. No. 13209.

336 mm. × 395 mm. Water-colour. Signed: *Eug. Isabey.* Coll.: de Joinville.

438. The Royal Visit to King Louis Philippe, 1843. Queen Victoria receiving King Louis Philippe on the Royal Yacht, Sept. 2nd, 6 p.m. *Souvenir*, iv, p. 1 (c).

275 mm. × 437 mm. Water-colour. Signed: *E. Isabey, 1844.* Louis Philippe Souvenir. Reprod.: R. Davies, pl. iii (a).

439. The same. The Queen leaving Le Tréport in King Louis Philippe's launch, Sept. 7th, 8.30 a.m.

Souvenir, iv, p. 20 (a).

248 mm. × 335 mm. Water-colour. Signed: *E. Isabey, 1844.* Louis Philippe Souvenir. Reprod.: R. Davies, pl. viii (a).

ALPHONSE JACOB (? – ?).

440. Design for a drawing-room. No. 17185.

180 mm. × 260 mm. Pen, Indian ink and water-colour. Signed: *Alphonse Jacob, elève de Mr Percier.* Inscribed in pencil: *Salon de M. de Villette.*

441. Design for a boudoir. No. 17186.

231 mm. × 205 mm. Pen, Indian ink and water-colour. Signed: *Alphonse Jacob, Elève de Monsieur Percier.* Inscribed: *Boudoir de Me de Villete.*

Nothing is known of this pupil of Charles Percier (1764–1838), but he may have belonged to the family of furniture designers of the same name, with one of whom Percier collaborated. The paper of the drawings has a water-mark dated 1820 which is probably also approximately that of the drawings.

LOUIS GODEFROY JADIN (1805–1882).

442. Dead Game. No. 13210.

366 mm. × 516 mm. Water-colour. Signed: *G. Jadin.* Coll.: de Joinville.

MARIE VICTOIRE JAQUOTOT (1778–1855).

443. The Duke of Wellington, 1817. No. 13243.

c. 150 mm. × 120 mm. Oval. Pencil and grey wash. An inscription apparently cut from below the drawing and now attached to the frame reads: *Wellington d'après nature fait chez Mme. Jaquotot à Paris—en 1817.*

Cf. Lord G. Wellesley and J. Steegman, *The Iconography of the First Duke of Wellington*, 1935, p. 25, who also reproduce as frontispiece a version of this drawing, in enamel on porcelain signed and dated 1817, in the possession of Capt. Berkeley Williams.

CHARLES HENRI ALFRED JOHANNOT (1800–1837).

444. In a Library. No. 13211.

114 mm. × 78 mm. Water-colour. Signed: *Alfred Johannot.* Coll.: de Joinville.

TONY JOHANNOT (1803–1852).

445. Conversation Galante. No. 13213.

283 mm. × 245 mm. Water-colour. Signed: *Tony Johannot 1831.* Coll.: de Joinville.

446. A nun, seated. No. 13212.

237 mm. × 169 mm. Pencil. Signed: *Tony Johannot 1838.* Coll.: de Joinville.

447. A fishergirl. No. 13214.

240 mm. × 176 mm. Water-colour. Signed: *Tony Johannot 1839.* Coll.: de Joinville.

448. The Royal Visit to King Louis Philippe, 1843. The tour of the gallery on the ground floor, Château d'Eu. *Souvenir*, iv, p. 13 (c).

328 mm. × 447 mm. Water-colour. Signed: *Tony Johannot 1844.* Louis Philippe Souvenir. Reprod.: R. Davies, pl. vii (a).

King Louis Philippe with Queen Victoria, followed by Queen Marie with the Prince Consort, inspecting the tapestry after Le Brun's 'Death of Meleager' presented to the Queen by King Louis Philippe and preserved at Windsor.

FRANÇOIS FERDINAND PHILIPPE LOUIS MARIE D'ORLEANS, PRINCE DE JOINVILLE (1818–1900).

449. The Princes and Princesses of Portugal playing with a miniature carriage on a terrace. No. 13177.

168 mm. × 275 mm. Water-colour. Signed: *Fr. O mai 1850.*

Mentioned by Queen Victoria in her diary (June 1st, 1850) as 'charming' and 'so cleverly and prettily done'. The artist was the third son of King Louis Philippe. In England after 1848. Three water-colours of Devonshire scenes by him are in *Souvenir Album*, v, p. 59.

PIERRE EUGENE LACOSTE (1818–1908).

450. La Vie de Paris en 1848. I. Liberté de la Parole. No. 13147.

233 mm. × 331 mm. Pen and water-colour. Signed: *Eugène Lacoste.* Inscribed: as given above.

Fig. 14. E. LAMI: Presentations to Queen Victoria at the Château d'Eu. Catalogue No. 463

Fig. 15. E. LAMI: The Salon de Famille, Château d'Eu. Catalogue No. 464

451. The same. II. Qui donne au pauvre, prête à Dieu.
No. 13148.

230 mm. × 330 mm. Pen and water-colour. Signed: *Eugène Lacoste*. Inscribed: as given above.

452. The same. III. Heure des Repas. No. 13149.

230 mm. × 330 mm. Pen and light water-colour. Signed: *Eugène Lacoste*. Inscribed: as given above.

453. The same. IV. Ateliers Nationaux. Heure de Travail. No. 13150.

232 mm. × 330 mm. Pen and water-colour. Signed: *Eugène Lacoste*. Inscribed: as given above.

454. The same. V. Préfecture de Police.
Fig. 12. No. 13151.

232 mm. × 330 mm. Pen and water-colour. Signed: *E. Lacoste*. Inscribed: *Préfecture de police sous Caussidière* (?).

455. The same. VI. Refreshment. No. 13152.

230 mm. × 330 mm. Pen and light wash. Signed: *Eugène Lacoste*. Inscribed: *Lapin au Cirage, Veau froid et autres*.

456. The same. VII. An arrest. No. 13153.

230 mm. × 328 mm. Pen and water-colour. Signed: *Eugène Lacoste*. Inscribed: *Tu ne sens pas la poudre, toi. Tu sens l'encre.*

457. The same. VIII. Deux Frères!!! No. 13154.

230 mm. × 331 mm. Pen and water-colour. Signed: *Eugène Lacoste*. Inscribed: as given above.

JEAN EDOUARD LACRETELLE (1817–1900).

458. Princess Charlotte of Belgium, 1849. No. 13178.
Circular, diameter 170 mm. Water-colour. Signed: *E. Lacretelle.*

458a. Portrait of Albert Edward, Prince of Wales, later King Edward VII. No. 13046.

579 mm. × 432 mm. Water-colours. Coll.: H.R.H. Princess Louise, Duchess of Argyll; H.R.H. The Duke of Kent.

EUGENE LOUIS LAMI (1800–1890).

459. The Royal Visit to King Louis Philippe, 1843.
The Queen of the French receiving Queen Victoria at Le Tréport, Saturday, Sept. 2nd, 6.30 p.m.
Souvenir, iv, p. 2 (*a*).

166 mm. × 267 mm. Water-colour. Signed: *Eug. Lami 1843.* Inscribed: *Welcome Victoria* in pencil on border. Lemoisne, 1914. No. 496. Reprod.: R. Davies, pl. iii (*b*).

Sketch of the same scene as that depicted in the finished water-colour No. 460.

460. The same. The Reception of Queen Victoria by the King and Queen of the French on landing at Le Tréport. *Souvenir*, iv, p. 2 (*b*).

228 mm. × 364 mm. Water-colour. Signed: *Eugène Lami*. Louis Philippe Souvenir. Lemoisne, 1914, No. 495.

Presentations to Her Majesty, 6.30 p.m. The Queen of Belgium, The Duchesse d'Orléans, Madame Adelaïde, the Prince and Princesse de Joinville, the Duc d'Aumale, the Duchess of Saxe Coburg, the Duc de Montpensier and others.

The Royal Accounts in the Louvre mention a commission to Lami for four drawings at 6,000 fr., 30th Sept., 1843.

461. The same. The Arrival of Queen Victoria at Le Tréport, Sept. 2nd, 6.30 p.m. *Fig. 13.* *Souvenir*, iv, p. 3.

351 mm. × 610 mm. Water-colour. Signed: *Eug. Lami.* Louis Philippe Souvenir. Lemoisne, 1914. No. 498. Reprod.: Lemoisne, 1912, p. 66; R. Davies, pl. iv (*b*).

The Royal party before a tent on the quay below the church. An enlargement in oil, with variations, at Versailles commissioned by King Louis Philippe.

462. The same. The arrival of Queen Victoria at the Château d'Eu. Sept. 2nd, 7 p.m. *Souvenir*, iv, p. 4.

362 mm. × 552 mm. Water-colour. Signed: *Eugène Lami*. Louis Philippe Souvenir. Lemoisne, 1914, No. 500.

An enlargement in oil is at Versailles, commissioned by King Louis Philippe (reproduced Lemoisne, 1912, p. 72).

463. The same. Presentations to Queen Victoria in the Galerie des Guises, Château d'Eu, Saturday, Sept. 2nd, 9 p.m. *Fig. 14. Souvenir*, iv, p. 8 (*b*).

260 mm. × 450 mm. Water-colour. Signed: *Eugène Lami 1843.* Louis Philippe Souvenir. Lemoisne, 1914, No. 502. Reprod.: Lemoisne, 1912, p. 68.

464. The same. Salon de Famille, Château d'Eu.
Fig. 15. Souvenir, iv, p. 9 (*b*).

276 mm. × 433 mm. Water-colour. Signed: *Eugène Lami 1843.* Louis Philippe Souvenir. Lemoisne, 1914, No. 504. Reprod.: R. Davies, pl. vi (*a*).

The two Queens at a round table with Madame Adelaïde, the Duchesse d'Orléans, the Duc d'Aumale and the Duchesse de Nemours. The King with the Prince Consort on a sofa to left attended by Lord Aberdeen, Mons. Guizot and others.

An enlargement in oil with variations painted to the Royal command and exhibited at the Salon of 1846 (No. 1058) was owned by the Duc de Vendôme.

465. The same. Concert in the Galerie des Guises, Château d'Eu, Sept. 4th, 9 p.m.
Fig. 16. Souvenir, iv, p. 18 (*b*).

Fig. 16. E. LAMI: Concert at the Château d'Eu. Catalogue No. 465

Fig. 17. E. LAMI: The French Royal Family at Claremont. Catalogue No. 473

274 mm. × 404 mm. Water-colour. Signed: *E.Lami 1843*. Louis Philippe Souvenir. Lemoisne, 1914, No. 507. Reprod.: Lemoisne, 1912, p. 70.

The Royal Party seated at a table in the foreground, the orchestra to the right with the conductor Girard and two singers. An enlargement in oil, commissioned by the King on June 6th, 1844, was in the collection of the Duc de Vendôme.

466. The same. A carabinier of the First Regiment.
Souvenir, iv, p. 16.

396 mm. × 298 mm. Pencil and slight colour wash. Signed: *Eug. Lami 1843*. Inscribed: *Soldat du 1er Régiment de Carabiniers passé en revue par le Prince Albert, à la ville d'Eu le 5 septembre 1843* (cf. No. 368).

467. Louis d'Orléans, Duc de Nemours, in uniform.
No. 13161.

255 mm. × 190 mm. Pencil and water-colour. Signed: *E. Lami, 1844*.

468. 'The Duc de Nemours in the costume that he wore at the Ball on 6th June, 1845.' No. 13179.

394 mm. × 270 mm. Pencil and water-colour. Signed: *Eugène Lami 1845*. Lemoisne, 1914, No. 1096.

The Ball on June 6th, 1845, was at Buckingham Palace.

Two examples were commissioned for 600 fr. by King Louis Philippe, July 3rd, 1846, one for presentation to Queen Victoria.

A reduced copy by Dalton is also at Windsor (No. 13162).

469. 'The Duchesse de Nemours in the costume that she wore at the Ball on 6th June, 1845.' No. 13180.

374 mm. × 277 mm. Pen and water-colour. Signed: *Eugène Lami 1845*. Lemoisne, 1914, No. 1097.

Two examples were commissioned for 600 fr. by King Louis Philippe, one for presentation to Queen Victoria, July 3rd, 1846.

A reduced copy by Dalton is also at Windsor (No. 13163).

470. The Staircase at Buckingham Palace; the Court Ball of July 5th, 1848. *Souvenir*, ii, p. 37.

380 mm. × 335 mm. Water-colour. Signed: *Eug. Lami*. Lemoisne, 1914, No. 538; Reprod.: R. Davies, pl. xii (*a*).

471. The Christening of Arthur, Duke of Connaught, in the Chapel of Buckingham Palace, 1850.
Souvenir, ii, p. 43.

160 mm. × 375 mm. Water-colour. Signed: *Eugène Lami*. Lemoisne, 1914, No. 548. Reprod.: Lemoisne, 1912, p. 118.

The Royal Family in the centre, the Archbishop of Canterbury officiating, and the god-parents, the Duchess of Kent, the Duke of Wellington and the Crown Prince of Prussia to the right.

A sketch with variations (cf. Lemoisne, 1914, No. 547) was in the collection of M. Beraldi.

472. The Duc and Duchesse de Nemours and their children, the Comte d'Eu, Duc d'Alençon, and Princesse Marguerite, 1850. No. 13165.

203 mm. × 265 mm. Water-colour. Signed: *Eugène Lami 1850*.

473. The French Royal Family at Claremont, May 1850.
Fig. 17. Souvenir, iv, p. 26.

270 mm. × 372 mm. Water-colour. Signed: *Eug. Lami 1850*. Lemoisne, 1914, No. 552. Reprod.: Lemoisne, 1912, p. 114.

As mentioned by Queen Victoria in her Diary (May 24th, 1850), a birthday present from the King and Queen of the French.

474. Costume Ball at Buckingham Palace, 13th June, 1851. *Souvenir*, ii, p. 38.

310 mm. × 455 mm. Water-colour. Signed: *Eugène Lami. 1851*. Lemoisne, 1914, No. 542. Reprod.: R. Davies, pl. xiv (*a*).

Costumes of the period of Charles II. Queen Victoria with the Prince Consort on the right.

475. The Royal Visit to the Emperor Napoleon III, 1855. The Supper in the Salle des Spectacles, Versailles, Aug. 25th. *Souvenir*, iv, p. 58.

515 mm. × 378 mm. Water-colour. Signed: *Eugène Lami 1855*. Napoleon III 1855 Souvenir. Lemoisne, 1914, No. 519; Dussieux, p. 295. Reprod.: R. Davies, pl. xxi.

Replica, with variations, in the Louvre (Reprod.: Lemoisne, 1912, p. 160).

476. Victoria, Princess Royal. No. 13164.

254 mm. × 194 mm. Water-colour on grey paper.

477. Historical or costume scene. No. 13230.

228 mm. × 358 mm. Water-colour. Signed: *Eugène Lami 1883*.

See also p. 68 under Eugène, and No. 512.

EUGENE LAMI and CAMILLE ROQUEPLAN (1800–1855).

478. The Royal Visit to King Louis Philippe, 1843. The Staircase at the Château d'Eu.
Fig. 18. Souvenir, iv, p. 8 (*a*).

357 mm. × 268 mm. Water-colour. Louis Philippe Souvenir. Lemoisne, 1914, No. 506.

The Royal Company descending, headed by the King with Queen Victoria and the Queen with the Prince Consort.

Fig. 18. E. LAMI and C. ROQUEPLAN: Queen Victoria at the Château d'Eu. Catalogue No. 478

EUGENE LAMI and JULES PIERRE MICHEL DIETERLE (1811–1869).

479. The Royal Visit to the Emperor Napoleon III, 1855. Gala Performance at the Opera in Paris, Aug. 21st. *Souvenir*, iv, p. 46.

357 mm. × 570 mm. Water-colour. Inscribed: *Eugène Lami & Dieterle*. Napoleon III 1855 Souvenir. Lemoisne, 1914, No. 516; Dussieux, p. 295. Reprod.: Lemoisne, 1912, p. 154.

The Royal party in their box on the right.

EUGENE LAMI (Attributed to).

480. Costume Ball at Marlborough House (?). No. 13231.

170 mm. × 332 mm. Pencil and body colour.

Not by Lami, perhaps a copy.

THEODORE LEBLANC (1800–1837).

481. Oriental camp scene with musicians. No. 13215.

202 mm. × 288 mm. Pen and water-colour. Signed: *Th. Leblanc*. Coll.: de Joinville.

D. LEBOUTEUX (active 1855) and JULES WORMS.

482. The Royal Visit to the Emperor Napoleon III, 1855. The Hôtel de Ville, Paris, fountains in the Salon de la Paix et de l'Empereur. *Souvenir*, iv, p. 51 (*b*).

266 mm. × 198 mm. Water-colour. Inscribed: *Lebouteux. Worms*.

Lebouteux appears to be unrecorded.

483. The same. The Hôtel de Ville, Paris, fountain in the Salon des Quatre Colonnes. *Souvenir*, iv, p. 52 (*b*).

267 mm. × 198 mm. Water-colour. Inscribed: 1855 *Lebouteux. Worms*.

484. The same. The Hôtel de Ville, Paris, Salon de l'Empereur. *Souvenir*, iv, p. 53 (*a*).

296 mm. × 395 mm. Water-colour. Signed: *1855 D. Lebouteux*. Inscribed: *Figures par Worms*.

ACHILLE LE CLERC (1785–1853).

485. Four designs for the entrance to, and rooms in, a palace. Nos. 13047–50.

c. 200 mm. × 320 mm. Pen, Indian ink and water-colour. Signed: *A. Le Clerc architecte*, and inscribed in pencil on the mount: *From Lord Fife 1815*.

PIERRE BERNARD LEFRANC (1795–1856).

486. Three drawings of the dining-room at the Château de Neuilly. Nos. 17189–91.

166–231 mm. × 384–503 mm. Pen, Indian ink and water-colour. Signed and inscribed by the architect as surveyor to the Duc d'Orléans.

The drawings are probably connected with the alterations made in the Château for Louis Philippe, as Duc d'Orléans, between 1820 and 1823.

LEROUX (active 1855) and JULES WORMS.

487. The Royal Visit to the Emperor Napoleon III, 1855. The Hôtel de Ville, Paris, Aug. 23rd, double staircase to the Library. *Souvenir*, iv, p. 52 (*a*).

267 mm. × 200 mm. Water-colour. Inscribed: *Leroux*.

488. The same. The Hôtel de Ville, Paris, Salon des Arcades. *Souvenir*, iv, p. 53 (*b*).

297 mm. × 398 mm. Water-colour. Signed: *Leroux 1855*. Inscribed: *Figures par Worms*.

Leroux is not to be identified with certainty among several of the name.

PROSPER GEORGES ANTOINE MARILHAT (1811–1847).

489. Street scene in Cairo. No. 13216.

286 mm. × 214 mm. Water-colour. Signed: *P. Marilhat*. Coll.: de Joinville.

490. The Royal Visit to King Louis Philippe, 1843. The Return from the Mont d'Orléans, Monday, Sept. 4th; approaching Le Tréport. *Souvenir*, iv, p. 14 (*b*).

302 mm. × 452 mm. Water-colour. Signed: *P. Marilhat*. Louise Philippe Souvenir. Reprod.: R. Davies, pl. vi (*b*).

An enlargement, with variations, in oil and in collaboration with Lami is at Versailles (cf. Lemoisne, 1912, p. 74, and reproduction).

FRANÇOIS MEURET (1800–1887).

491. The Princes Philip and Augustus of Saxe Coburg and Gotha at the ages of two and one year, 1846. No. 13168.

260 mm. × 210 mm. Water-colour. Signed: *Meuret*.

Sons of Prince Augustus of Saxe Coburg and Gotha and Princesse Clémentine d'Orléans.

492. Princesse Marguerite d'Orléans, daughter of the Duc and Duchesse de Nemours (cf. No. 504) at the age of fourteen months, 1847. No. 13169.

234 mm. × 195 mm. Water-colour. Signed: *f. Meuret*.

493. Prince Ferdinand d'Orléans, second son of the Duc and Duchesse de Nemours at the age of 11 months. No. 13167.

164 mm. × 150 mm. Water-colour. Signed: *Meuret*.

FRANÇOIS MEURET (After).

494. The Duchesse de Nemours, 1848.   No. 13170.

272 mm. × 212 mm. Water-colour. Inscribed: *Faija copied.*
Copy after Meuret by Faija.

495. Gaston d'Orléans, Comte d'Eu, when a year and
a half old.   No. 13166.

185 mm. × 138 mm. Water-colour.
Copy by Dalton, 1843, after Meuret.

EMMANUEL ADOLPHE MIDY (1797–1874).

496. French peasant interior.   No. 13217.

230 mm. × 274 mm. Water-colour. Signed: *Ad. Midy.*
Coll.: de Joinville.

ANTOINE LEON MOREL-FATIO (1810–1871).

497. The Royal Visit to King Louis Philippe, 1843.
The King leaving Le Tréport to greet Queen Victoria,
5.30 p.m., Sept. 2nd.   *Souvenir,* iv, p. 1 (*b*).

186 mm. × 375 mm. Water-colour. Signed: *L. Morel-
Fatio* with anchor. Louis Philippe Souvenir.
Subject exhibited by the artist at the Salon of 1846.

498. The Royal Visit to the Emperor Napoleon III,
1855. The landing of Queen Victoria at Boulogne,
Aug. 18th.   *Souvenir,* iv, p. 39 (*b*).

315 mm. × 495 mm. Water-colour. Signed: *Morel-Fatio*
with anchor. Napoleon III 1855 Souvenir. Literature:
Dussieux, p. 295.

CHARLES LOUIS MOZIN (1806–1862).

499. The Royal Visit to the Emperor Napoleon III,
1855. The yacht 'Victoria and Albert' entering Boulogne
Harbour, Aug. 18th.   *Souvenir,* iv, p. 39 (*a*).

327 mm. × 505 mm. Water-colour. Signed: *Ch. Mozin
1855.* Napoleon III 1855 Souvenir. Literature: Dussieux,
p. 295.

ALPHONSE MARIE ADOLPHE DE NEUVILLE
(1835–1885).

500. An infantryman presenting arms.   No. 13157.

205 mm. × 105 mm. Pen on brown paper. Signed:
A. de Neuville.

FRANÇOIS JOSEPH NOLAU (1804–1883).

501. The Royal Visit to King Louis Philippe, 1843.
Queen Victoria's dressing room at the Château d'Eu.
                             Souvenir, iv, p. 7 (*a*).

212 mm. × 257 mm. Water-colour. Signed: *Nolau.* Louis
Philippe Souvenir.

502. The same. The Prince Consort's dressing room at
the Château d'Eu.   *Souvenir,* iv, p. 7 (*b*).

225 mm. × 353 mm. Water-colour. Signed: *Nolau.* Louis
Philippe Souvenir.

503. The same. The dining room, the Château d'Eu.
                             Souvenir, iv, p. 9 (*a*).

230 mm. × 380 mm. Water-colour. Signed: *Nolau.* Louis
Philippe Souvenir.

PRINCESSE MARGUERITE D'ORLEANS, COUN-
TESS CZARTORYSKI (1846–1893).

504. Queen Victoria holding the infant Prince Albert
Victor in her arms at his christening.   *Fig. 20.*

Album, *Drawings of the Princes and Princesses,* last page.

345 mm. × 245 mm. Pencil, water-colour and Chinese
white. Signed: *Marguerite d'Orléans 10 mars 1864.*

The artist was the daughter of the Duc de Nemours
(cf. No. 492).

PIERRE JUSTIN OUVRIE (1806–1879).

505. The Royal Visit to the Emperor Napoleon III,
1855. Versailles from the Pièce d'eau des Suisses.
                             Souvenir, iv, p. 45 (*a*).

312 mm. × 470 mm. Water-colour. Signed: *Justin Ouvrié
1855.* Commissioned 1855 (800 fr.).

DOMINIQUE LOUIS FEREAL PAPETY
(1815–1849).

506. Italian peasant woman and child resting in a wood.
                                          No. 13218.

264 mm. × 198 mm. Oil on paper. Signed: *Dom Papety.*
Coll.: de Joinville.

BENOIT PECHEUX (1779–after 1831).

507. Louis XVIII entering Paris by the Porte St. Denis,
May, 1814.   No. 13141.

328 mm. × 460 mm. Water-colour. Signed: *B. Pecheux.*

508. The same from a nearer view-point.
                             Fig. 19. No. 13142.

337 mm. × 458 mm. Water-colour. Signed: *B. Pecheux.*

CHARLES OLIVIER DE PENNE (1831–1897).

509. Bloodhounds in a kennel.   No. 13160.

287 mm. × 445 mm. Water-colour. Signed: *Ol. de Penne.*

CHARLES FRANÇOIS PENSEE (1799–1871).

510. The Royal Visit to the Emperor Napoleon III,
1855. Villeneuve l'Etang, the Lake, 26th Aug.
                             Souvenir, iv, p. 59 (*a*).

325 mm. × 473 mm. Water-colour. Signed: *Cles Pensée.*
Commissioned 1855 (400 fr.).

Fig. 19. B. PECHEUX: The entry of Louis XVIII into Paris. Catalogue No. 508

511. The same. Villeneuve l'Etang, the Château.
Souvenir, iv, p. 59 (*b*).

325 mm. × 473 mm. Water-colour. Signed: *Cles Pensée.*
Commissioned 1855 (400 fr.).

OLIVIER PICHAT (?–1912).

A water-colour with this name and dated 1869, from the
Duke of Connaught's collection, Bagshot, is in *Military
Costumes*, xii, p. 51.

'R. DE QUERELLES.'

A series of drawings (12 plus title, c. 275 mm. ×
217 mm.) Nos. 16875–16887 in *Military Costumes*,
v, pp. 111 ff. in pencil and red chalk, entitled *Une
Carrière Contemporaine. Vie Politique et Militaire de Jean-
Baptiste Pistolard* and satirizing the rise and fall of a
Napoleonic Marshal is signed with this name. An
unsigned and undated note says that the drawings *have
been in the owner's possession for ten years* and that *le Vicomte
de Querelle has been dead some years ago*, but as the name is
not recorded either in d'Hozier *Noblesse Française* or in
biographic dictionaries, and as the drawings show very
considerable ability, it seems probable that 'de Querelles'

is a pseudonym for one of the practised caricaturists in
lithography of the period 1830–40.

CHARLES AUGUSTE QUESTEL (1807–1888) and EUGENE LAMI.

512. The Royal Visit to the Emperor Napoleon III,
1855. Illuminations in the Gardens of Versailles, 25th
August.   *Souvenir*, iv, p. 56 *verso*.

283 mm. × 500 mm. Water-colour. Inscribed: *Ch. Questel
Arch . . . . & E. Lami.* Napoleon III 1855 Souvenir.
Dussieux, p. 295.

Questel, architect to the Palace of Versailles, was in
charge of the decorations etc. on the occasion of the
Royal Visit in 1855.

CHARLES RAMELET (1805–1851).

513. Breton peasants in a market place.   No. 13219.
260 mm. × 280 mm. Water-colour. Signed: *Ch. Ramelet.*
Coll.: de Joinville.

CHARLES CAIUS RENOUX (1795–1846).

514. The Royal Visit to King Louis Philippe, 1843. The
Chapel, the Château d'Eu.   *Souvenir*, iv, p. 13 (*b*).

282 mm. × 227 mm. Water-colour. Signed: *Renoux 1844*.
Louis Philippe Souvenir.

CHARLES CAIUS RENOUX and FRANZ XAVIER WINTERHALTER.

515. The same. Sitting room of Madame Adelaïde, the
Château d'Eu.   *Souvenir*, iv, p. 18 (*a*).

220 mm. × 294 mm. Water-colour. Signed: *Renoux 1844*.
Louis Philippe Souvenir.

Madame Adelaïde greeting Queen Victoria and the
Prince Consort.

CAMILLE JOSEPH ETIENNE ROQUEPLAN (1800–1845).

516. Landscape with windmills and travellers.
                                               No. 13220.

127 mm. × 230 mm. Water-colour. Signed: *Clle. Roqueplan*.
Coll.: de Joinville. Exhibited: Burlington Fine Arts Club,
1937, No. 188.

517. Shipping off the coast.   No. 13221.

197 mm. × 271 mm. Water-colour. Signed: *Camille
Roqueplan*. Coll.: de Joinville. Exhibited: Burlington Fine
Arts Club, 1937, No. 187.

518. Peasant children on a terrace.   No. 13222.

173 mm. × 130 mm. Water-colour. Signed: *Clle. Roqueplan*.
Coll.: de Joinville.

See also No. 478.

HENRI EDMOND RUDAUX (?–1927).

519. H.M. Queen Mary.   No. 13172.

362 mm. × 270 mm. Pencil. Signed: *Henri Rudaux 1916*.

520. H.R.H. Princess Mary (later Princess Royal and
Countess of Harewood), 1916.   No. 13173.

Circular, diameter 230 mm. Pencil and water-colour
Signed: *Henri Rudaux*.

ARY SCHEFFER (1795–1858).

521. A Village School.   No. 13223.

160 mm. × 217 mm. Pen and water-colour. Signed
(partly cut away): *Ary Scheffer*. Coll.: de Joinville.

HIPPOLYTE VICTOR VALENTIN SEBRON (1801–1879).

522. The Royal Visit to King Louis Philippe, 1843. The
Royal Party visiting the tombs of the Comtes d'Eu in
the crypt of St. Laurent.   *Souvenir*, iv, p. 17 (*a*).

192 mm. × 269 mm. Water-colour. Louis Philippe
Souvenir.

SIMONET.

523. Edward, Prince of Wales.   No. 13174.

334 mm. × 265 mm. Black chalk.

The artist appears to be unrecorded.

JEAN SORIEUL (1824–1871).

524. The Royal Visit to the Emperor Napoleon III,
1855. Review in the Champ de Mars by the Emperor
and the Prince Consort in the presence of the Empress
and Queen Victoria, August 24th.   *Souvenir*, iv, p. 55 (*b*).

325 mm. × 497 mm. Water-colour. Signed: *J. Sorieul
1855*. Napoleon III 1855 Souvenir. Dussieux, p. 295.

JACQUES FRANÇOIS JOSE SWEBACH (called DES FONTAINES) (1769–1823).

525. Death of General Desaix at the Battle of Marengo.
                                  Military Costumes, iv, p. 89.

517 mm. × 686 mm. Indian ink and blue wash. Signed:
Swebach an 9.

JAMES JACQUES JOSEPH TISSOT (1836–1902).

526. Albert Edward, Prince of Wales.   No. 13232.

300 mm. × 182 mm. Water-colour. Signed: *T*.

MAX VAUTIER (1828–?).

527. The Royal Visit to the Emperor Napoleon III,
1855. The Hôtel de Ville, Paris, August 23rd, the grand
Vestibule.   *Souvenir*, iv, p. 47 (*a*).

298 mm. × 397 mm. Water-colour. Signed: *Vautier*.
Reprod.: R. Davies, pl. xx (*a*).

528. The same. The Hôtel de Ville, Paris, the central
courtyard with the Staircase of Honour.
                                       Souvenir, iv, p. 48 (*b*).

444 mm. × 344 mm. Water-colour.

ANTOINE CHARLES HORACE (called CARLE) VERNET (1758–1836).

529. Départ de la Diligence.   No. 13144.

332 mm. × 492 mm. Water-colour.

530. La Chasse au Renard.   No. 13145.

303 mm. × 418 mm. Water-colour. Signed: *C. Vernet*.
Engraved in aquatint by Levachez (cf. A. Dayot, *Carle
Vernet*, 1925, p. 68, No. 12*d*).

531. La Chasse au Renard.   No. 13146.

292 mm. × 408 mm. Water-colour. Signed: *C. Vernet*.
Engraved in aquatint by Levachez (cf. A. Dayot, *Carle
Vernet*, 1925, p. 70, No. 12*e*).

Twenty-three water-colours of uniforms by this artist are
in *Military Costumes*, iv, and one in Vol. v.

HORACE VERNET (1789–1863).

532. Marengo, 1800. A company of foot in line before Napoleon.   No. 13227.

64 mm. × 86 mm. Miniature in gouache on blue paper.

Inscribed on mount: *Horace Vernet fect. 1837*, with title as given.

533. Austerlitz, 1805.   No 13228.

67 mm. × 90 mm. Miniature in gouache on blue paper.

Inscribed on mount: *Horace Vernet fect. 1837*, with title as given.

Thirteen water-colours of uniforms by this artist are in *Military Costumes*, iv.

EDOUARD AUGUSTE VILLAIN (1829–?) and JULES WORMS.

534. The Royal Visit to the Emperor Napoleon III, 1855. The Hôtel de Ville, Paris, one of the Fountains in the recesses of the Galerie des Fêtes.

Souvenir iv, p. 50 (*a*).

266 mm. × 198 mm. Water-colour. Signed: *Villain 1855*.

Inscribed: *Figures par Worms*.

JULES WORMS (1832–?).

See Nos. 373, 403, 404, 422, 423, 434, 435, 482, 483, 484, 487, 488, 534.

ANONYMOUS ARTIST, EARLY NINETEENTH CENTURY.

535. Entrance to a fortified town.   No. 13156.

204 mm. × 365 mm. Pen and water-colour.

ANONYMOUS ARTIST (c. 1815).

536. Monsieur La Gobe! ou la Croquade de Jacques de Falaise, faite d'après Nature, sur le Théâtre de Mr Comte.   No. 13241.

214 mm. × 315 mm. Water-colour.

ANONYMOUS ARTIST (c. 1821).

537. Two designs for a ball room.   Nos. 17187–8.

415 mm. × 605 mm. Pen, Indian ink and water-colour.

The paper is water-marked 1821. The style of the architecture and decoration suggests that the drawings may be by a pupil of Percier or Fontaine working for a foreign patron, perhaps in Russia.

ANONYMOUS ARTIST (1855).

538. The Royal Visit to the Emperor Napoleon III. The Review in the Champs de Mars.   No. 13045.

229 mm. × 299 mm. Pencil and oils on paper. Coll.: H.R.H. Princess Louise, Duchess of Argyll; H.R.H. The Duke of Kent.

ADDENDUM

NICOLAS POUSSIN (1594–1665).

183a. The Entombment.   No. 0748.

140 mm. × 255 mm. Pen and bistre with bistre and grey wash over some black and red chalk. Torn and mended.

III, 3.

The dead body of Christ is stretched across the foreground. Behind it the fainting Virgin is supported by St. John and one of the holy women. At the feet of Christ kneels the Magdalene in passionate grief. Behind her is the tomb over which bend two mourning figures. On the left against the sky two crosses are visible, on one of which leans a ladder with a man standing on it. The right-hand half of the composition is closed by a building with a door.

In general disposition and grouping the drawing is connected with the painting at Munich (Grautoff No. 20). In the painting, however, the character of the composition is altered by the much freer attitude of the body of Christ, which in the drawing is entirely stiff. Other alterations also occur. The Magdalene is moved to the left and placed behind the main group; St. John, one of the women and one of the men by the tomb are left out; two weeping putti are added at the feet of Christ; the crosses disappear, and the background consists entirely of landscape.

The painting dates from 1628–30, and the style of the drawing suggests the same period. The mixture of techniques, the coarse but expressive line, the curious convention for the drawing of the feet, and the vigorous use of wash are all characteristic of Poussin's style just before 1630. The drawing is highly finished and is not so much a working sketch as a complete rendering of the theme, like the Marino drawings.

Fig. 20. PRINCESSE MARGUERITE D'ORLEANS
Queen Victoria holding the infant Prince Albert Victor in her
arms at his christening, 1864. Catalogue No. 504

PLATES

I. FRANÇOIS CLOUET (*after*): Scene from a French farce. Catalogue No. 3

2. ETIENNE DELAUNE (*attributed to*): Design for a cup
Catalogue No. 4

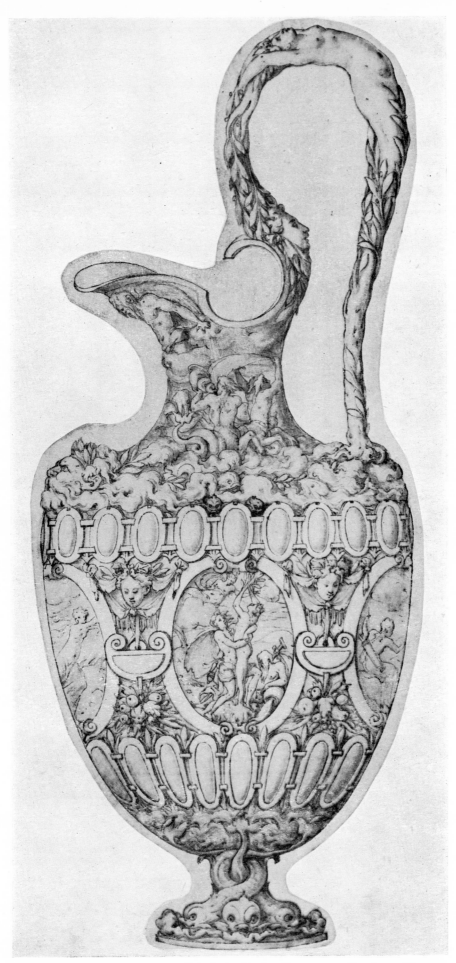

3. ETIENNE DELAUNE (*attributed to*): Design for a ewer. Catalogue No. 5

5. FRANÇOIS QUESNEL (*attributed to*): Portrait of a woman
Catalogue No. 13

4. FRANÇOIS QUESNEL (*attributed to*): Portrait of a young man
Catalogue No. 9

6. SECOND SCHOOL OF FONTAINEBLEAU: Rinaldo leaving Armida. Catalogue No. 20

7. JACQUES CALLOT: The Palazzo Pitti. Catalogue No. 22

8. JACQUES CALLOT: La Rue Neuve de Nancy. Catalogue No. 23

9. JACQUES CALLOT: A man playing dice
Catalogue No. 27

10. JACQUES CALLOT: Two men
Catalogue No. 30

11. JACQUES CALLOT: Two seated men
Catalogue No. 28

12. JACQUES CALLOT: Study of a man. Catalogue No. 24

13. JACQUES CALLOT: Study of a man. Catalogue No. 25

14. NICOLAS POUSSIN: Acis transformed into a river-god. Catalogue No. 160

15. NICOLAS POUSSIN: Dryope. Catalogue No. 156

16. NICOLAS POUSSIN: The Birth of Priapus. Catalogue No. 162

17. NICOLAS POUSSIN: Orpheus in Hades. Catalogue No. 157

18. NICOLAS POUSSIN: The Death of Chione. Catalogue No. 158

19. NICOLAS POUSSIN: Thetis and Achilles. Catalogue No. 161

20. NICOLAS POUSSIN: Polyphemus, Acis and Galatea. Catalogue No. 159

21. NICOLAS POUSSIN: Apollo guarding the herds of Admetus. Catalogue No. 155

H

22. NICOLAS POUSSIN: The Birth of Adonis. Catalogue No. 154

24. NICOLAS POUSSIN: Mercury and Argus. Catalogue No. 163

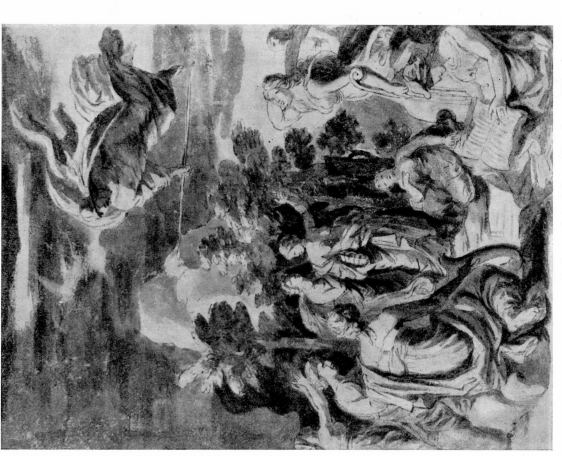

23. NICOLAS POUSSIN: Pallas and the Muses. Catalogue No. 164

25. NICOLAS POUSSIN: Battle of Romans and Sabines. Catalogue No. 167

26. NICOLAS POUSSIN: The Kingdom of Flora. Catalogue No. 169

27. NICOLAS POUSSIN: The Death of Camilla. Catalogue No. 165

28. NICOLAS POUSSIN: 'La Tintura del Corallo.' Catalogue No. 170

29. NICOLAS POUSSIN: Dance in honour of Pan. Catalogue No. 174

31. NICOLAS POUSSIN: Satyr and Child
Catalogue No. 177

30. NICOLAS POUSSIN: Nymph, Satyr and Cupid
Catalogue No. 176

32. NICOLAS POUSSIN: Diana hunting. Catalogue No. 178

33. NICOLAS POUSSIN: 'Le Fanciulle Rusticane'. Catalogue No. 179

34. NICOLAS POUSSIN: Battle of the Israelites and the Midianites. Catalogue No. 180

35. NICOLAS POUSSIN: The Victory of Godfrey de Bouillon. Catalogue No. 181

36. NICOLAS POUSSIN: God the Father. Catalogue No. 184

37. NICOLAS POUSSIN: The Schoolmaster of Falerii. Catalogue No. 190

38. NICOLAS POUSSIN: The Ascension. Catalogue No. 183

39. NICOLAS POUSSIN: Three Nymphs. Catalogue No. 187

40. NICOLAS POUSSIN: The Saving of Pyrrhus. Catalogue No. 189

41. NICOLAS POUSSIN: The Death of Virginia. Catalogue No. 193

42. NICOLAS POUSSIN: Bacchus and Ariadne. Catalogue No. 194

43. NICOLAS POUSSIN: St. Mary of Egypt and St. Zosimus. Catalogue No. 195

44. NICOLAS POUSSIN: The Rape of the Sabines.
Catalogue No. 192

45. NICOLAS POUSSIN: The Rape of the Sabines. Catalogue No. 191

46. NICOLAS POUSSIN: The Agony in the Garden. Catalogue No. 196

47. NICOLAS POUSSIN: Dance in honour of Pan. Catalogue No. 199 verso

48. NICOLAS POUSSIN: The Indian Triumph of Bacchus. Catalogue No. 199 recto

49. NICOLAS POUSSIN: Bacchanal before a Temple. Catalogue No. 198

50. NICOLAS POUSSIN: Hercules and Deianeira. Catalogue No. 207

51. NICOLAS POUSSIN: Marriage. Catalogue No. 204

52. NICOLAS POUSSIN: Confirmation. Catalogue No. 205

53. NICOLAS POUSSIN: Moses and the Daughters of Jethro. Catalogue No. 209

54. NICOLAS POUSSIN: Scipio Africanus and the Pirates. Catalogue No. 211

55. NICOLAS POUSSIN: Holy Family. Catalogue No. 213

56. NICOLAS POUSSIN: Hercules and Theseus fighting the Amazons
Catalogue No. 214

57. NICOLAS POUSSIN (*Studio of*): Hercules and the Erymanthian Boar
Catalogue No. 255

58. NICOLAS POUSSIN: The Finding of Queen Zenobia. Catalogue No. 216

59. NICOLAS POUSSIN: Confirmation. Catalogue No. 215

60. NICOLAS POUSSIN: Medea killing her children. Catalogue No. 217

61. NICOLAS POUSSIN (*studio of*) : Medea killing her children. Catalogue No. 264

62. NICOLAS POUSSIN: The three Marys at the Sepulchre. Catalogue No. 221

63. NICOLAS POUSSIN: Moses striking the Rock. Catalogue No. 218

64. NICOLAS POUSSIN: The Sacrifice of Polyxena. Catalogue No. 220

65. NICOLAS POUSSIN (*studio of*): Scipio Africanus and the Pirates. Catalogue No. 251

66. NICOLAS POUSSIN (*studio of*): Rinaldo and Armida. Catalogue No. 226

67. NICOLAS POUSSIN (*studio of*): The Kingdom of Flora. Catalogue No. 223.

68. NICOLAS POUSSIN (*studio of*): Moses trampling on Pharaoh's Crown. Catalogue No. 262

69. NICOLAS POUSSIN (*studio of*): Confirmation. Catalogue No. 261

70. NICOLAS POUSSIN (*attributed to*) : Hill-town near Rome. Catalogue No. 222

71. NICOLAS POUSSIN (*school of*) : Italian Farm Buildings. Catalogue No. 274

72. CLAUDE GELLEE: The Marriage of Isaac and Rebecca. Catalogue No. 41

73. CLAUDE GELLEE: Acis and Galatea. Catalogue No. 42

74. CLAUDE GELLEE: The Temple of Apollo at Delphi. Catalogue No. 47

75. CLAUDE GELLEE: St. John the Baptist preaching. Catalogue No. 44

K *

76. CLAUDE GELLEE: The Apulian Shepherd. Catalogue No. 43 verso

77. CLAUDE GELLEE: The Apulian Shepherd. Catalogue No. 43 recto

78. CLAUDE GELLEE: Moses and the Burning Bush. Catalogue No. 45

79. CLAUDE GELLEE: The Crossing of the Red Sea. Catalogue No. 46

80. CLAUDE GELLEE: The Campo Vaccino
Catalogue No. 51

81. CLAUDE GELLEE: Roman arches and tower
Catalogue No. 54

82. CLAUDE GELLEE: The Basilica of Constantine
Catalogue No. 55

83. CLAUDE GELLEE: View of the Colosseum
Catalogue No. 53

84. CLAUDE GELLEE: SS. Giovanni e Paolo, Rome
Catalogue No. 58

85. CLAUDE GELLEE: View of the Colosseum
Catalogue No. 52

86. CLAUDE GELLEE: The landing of Æneas in Italy. Catalogue No. 48

88. CLAUDE GELLEE: The wall of a villa
Catalogue No. 50

87. CLAUDE GELLEE: S. Giorgio in Velabro
Catalogue No. 56

90. CLAUDE GELLEE: An artist drawing
Catalogue No. 59

89. CLAUDE GELLEE: A house in the Campagna
Catalogue No. 57

91. CLAUDE GELLEE: A valley with trees
Catalogue No. 60

92. CLAUDE GELLEE: The Banks of the Tiber
Catalogue No. 61

93. CLAUDE GELLEE: The Tomb of Cecilia Metella. Catalogue No. 62

94. CLAUDE GELLEE (*attributed to*) : Study of Trees. Catalogue No. 63

95. ISRAEL SILVESTRE: The Grotto at Meudon. Catalogue No. 296

96. GABRIEL PERELLE: Landscape. Catalogue No. 152

97. CHARLES SIMONNEAU: Landscape. Catalogue No. 298

98. ANONYMOUS ARTIST (c. 1650): 'Le Palais sur le Mont.' Catalogue No. 301

99. ANONYMOUS ARTIST (c. 1650): Studies of Chinese men. Catalogue No. 302

100. LAURENT DE LA HYRE: The Adoration of the Shepherds. Catalogue No. 135

101. JACQUES COURTOIS: A Battle outside a town. Catalogue No. 33

102. JACQUES COURTOIS: A Battle. Catalogue No. 34

103. EUSTACHE LE SUEUR: The Assumption. Catalogue No. 140

104. EUSTACHE LE SUEUR: The Gods of Olympus. Catalogue No. 144

106. EUSTACHE LE SUEUR: The Angel leaving Tobit
Catalogue No. 138

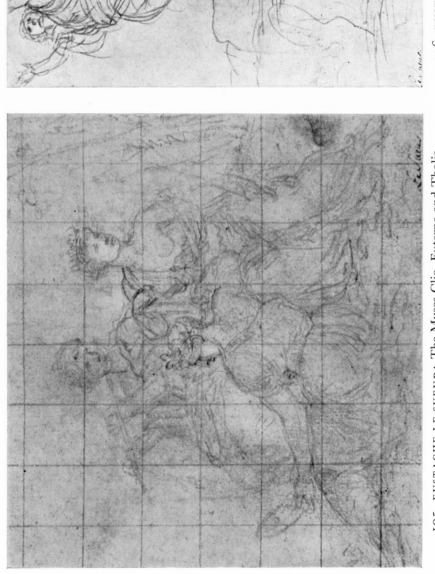

105. EUSTACHE LE SUEUR: The Muses Clio, Euterpe and Thalia
Catalogue No. 142

108. EUSTACHE LE SUEUR: The Ecstasy of St. Paul
Catalogue No. 141

107. EUSTACHE LE SUEUR: The Return from the Temple
Catalogue No. 139

109. EUSTACHE LE SUEUR: A Priest holding a mitre. Catalogue No. 146

110. CHARLES LEBRUN: Study for the head of a Persian. Catalogue No. 137

III. RAYMOND DE LA FAGE: The Rape of Helen. Catalogue No. 106

112. RAYMOND DE LA FAGE: Self-portrait. Catalogue No. 113

113. RAYMOND DE LA FAGE: Polyphemus, Acis and Galatea. Catalogue No. 111

114. RAYMOND DE LA FAGE: A battle. Catalogue No. 131

115. BERNARD PICART: A Lady resting. Catalogue No. 343

116. ANTOINE WATTEAU: A man in a turban. Catalogue No. 355

117. FRANÇOIS BOUCHER: Design for a frontispiece. Catalogue No. 311

118. CHARLES PARROCEL: Le Marquis de Beauvilliers. Catalogue No. 337

119. CHARLES PARROCEL: Studies of soldiers' heads. Catalogue No. 340

120. PHILIBERT BENOIT DE LA RUE: A Battle. Catalogue No. 325

121. ANONYMOUS ARTIST (c. 1780): Street Scene. Catalogue No. 363

123. LOUIS DE CARMONTELLE: Antoine Parmentier
Catalogue No. 313

122. LOUIS DE CARMONTELLE: Mme. Brissard
Catalogue No. 314

124–125. ELISABETH VIGEE-LEBRUN: Portraits of the Comtesse
and the Comte de Provence, Catalogue Nos. 354 and 353

126. FRANÇOIS DROUAIS (*attributed to*) : Portrait of the Dauphin, son of Louis XV (?)
Catalogue No. 318

127. J. M. MOREAU THE YOUNGER: Roger and Alcina
Catalogue No. 332

LIST OF NUMBERS

The first number is the Inventory Number. The second number is the Catalogue Number

Inventory No.	Cat. No.	Inventory No.	Cat. No.	Inventory No.	Cat. No.	Inventory No.	Cat. No.	Inventory No.	Cat. No.	Inventory No.	Cat. No.
036	179	6131	39	6210	91	11885	262	11938	162	11989	258
037	182	6133	38	6211	92	11886	211	11939	160	11990	172
038	228	6134	37	6212	94	11887	218	11940	159	11991	275
039	229	6140	222	6213	93	11888	193	11941	156	11992	227
0153	20	6141	274	6214	95	11889	210	11942	166	11993	279
0184	135	6152	361	6215	96	11890	209	11943	167	11994	278
0698	251	6163	150	6216	97	11891	280	11944	168	11995	200
0749	183	6164	147	6217	98	11892	217	11945	163	11996	273
0750	184	6165	148	6218	99	11893	264	11946	164	11997	196
0868	35	6166	146	6219	100	11894	204	11947	155	11998	270
01183	303	6167	149	6220	101	11895	216	11948	248	11999	64
3523	306	6168	138	6221	102	11896	205	11949	249	13043	357
3541	40	6169	143	6222	103	11897	215	11950	250	13044	312
3825a	116	6170	145	6223	104	11898	261	11951	242	13045	538
3825b	117	6171	142	6224	105	11899	260	11952	244	13046	458a
3826a	120	6172	139	6225	106	11900	266	11953	230	13047–50	485
3826b	122	6173	141	6226	107	11901	267	11954	235	13051	1
3827a	121	6175	140	6227	108	11902	219	11955	231	13052	4
3827b	123	6176	144	6228	110	11903	191	11956	240	13053	5
3828a	119	6177	342	6229	112	11904	192	11957	239	13055	7
3828b	118	6178	21	6230	109	11905	199	11958	241	13056	8
3829	129	6180	311	6231	111	11906	220	11959	237	13057	13
3948	355	6181	127	6328	130	11907	246	11960	243	13058	19
4337	327	6182	128	6329	131	11908	259	11961	238	13059	12
4500	300	6183	133	6340	36	11909	189	11962	245	13060	18
4614	22	6184	124	6343	34	11910	198	11963	236	13061	11
4615	23	6185	113	6344	33	11911	194	11964	233	13062	15
4624	26	6186	307	6445	3	11912	207	11965	234	13063	16
4625	27	6187	305	6566	285	11913	190	11966	232	13064	17
4626	29	6188	115	6567	286	11914	187	11967	212	13065	10
4627	28	6189	114	6568	287	11915	185	11968	212a	13066	9
4628	31	6190	132	6569	288	11916	197	11969	253	13067	14
4629	30	6191	134	6570	289	11917	208	11970	252	13068	2
4634	25	6192	73	6571	290	11919	206	11971	256	13069	6
4635	24	6193	74	6572	291	11920	214	11972	255	13070	351
4877a	221	6194	75	6576	301	11921	203	11973	254	13071	72
5167	137	6195	76	6598	299	11922	188	11974	268	13072	136
5187	151	6196	77	6599	298	11923	201	11975	175	13073	302
5723	281	6197	78	6762	153	11924	202	11976	226	13075	43
5794	292	6198	79	6803	32	11925	195	11977	265	13076	41
5795	293	6199	80	6840	125	11927	63	11978	269	13077	42
5796	294	6200	81	6841	126	11928	277	11979	174	13078	62
5803	66	6201	82	11876	247	11929	276	11980	176	13079	47
5806	68	6202	83	11877	224	11930	282	11981	177	13080	46
5808	65	6203	88	11878	223	11931	284	11982	171	13081	48
5811	70	6204	84	11879	225	11932	283	11983	169	13082	44
5812	295	6205	85	11880	263	11933	154	11984	170	13083	45
5814	356a	6206	86	11881	271	11934	161	11985	178	13084	50
5820	297	6207	87	11882	181	11935	158	11986	173	13085	51
5823	67	6208	89	11883	272	11936	165	11987	186	13086	52
6130	360	6209	90	11884	180	11937	157	11988	213	13087	54

Inventory No.	Cat No.	Inventory No.	Cat. No.	Inventory No.	Cat. No.	Inventory No.	Cat. No.	Inventory No.	Cat. No.	Inventory No.	Cat. No.
13088	53	13118	313	13144	529	13171	71	13205	425	13230	477
13089	55	13119	315	13145	530	13172	519	13206	429	13231	480
13090	56	13120	316	13146	531	13173	520	13207	432	13232	526
13091	57	13122	353	13147	450	13174	523	13208	433	13233	377
13092	59	13123	354	13148	451	13175	330	13209	437	13234	380
13093	60	13124	318	13149	452	13177	449	13210	442	13235	378
13094	61	13125	322	13150	453	13178	458	13211	444	13236	375
13095	49	13126	323	13151	454	13179	468	13212	446	13237	376
13096	58	13127	324	13152	455	13180	469	13213	445	13238	386
13098	152	13128	325	13153	456	13189	365	13214	447	13239	401
13099	69	13129	320	13154	457	13190	367	13215	481	13240	402
13101	296	13130	319	13155	436	13191	371	13216	489	13241	536
13103	343	13131	333	13156	535	13192	370	13217	496	13242	321
13105	345	13132	334	13157	500	13193	379	13218	506	13243	443
13106	344	13133	335	13158	399	13194	382	13219	513	13244	304
13108	346	13134	336	13159	400	13195	381	13220	516	17166	352
13109	347	13135	337	13160	509	13196	385	13221	517	17167	309
13110	348	13136	338	13161	467	13197	390	13222	518	17168	308
13111	349	13137	339	13164	476	13198	391	13223	521	17183	362
13112	363	13138	340	13165	472	13199	392	13224	310	17184	358
13113	328	13139	341	13166	495	13200	396	13225	331	17185	440
13114	329	13140	350	13167	493	13201	397	13226	332	17186	441
13115	359	13141	507	13168	491	13202	398	13227	532	17187–8	537
13116	317	13142	508	13169	492	13203	417	13228	533	17189–91	486
13117	314	13143	326	13170	494	13204	424	13229	374		

	Cat. No.		Cat. No.		Cat. No.
Souvenir Volume, ii, p. 37	470	Souvenir Volume, iv, p. 17a	522	Souvenir Volume iv, p. 51a	435
ii, p. 38	474	iv, p. 17b	395	iv, p. 51b	482
ii, p. 43	471	iv, p. 18a	515	iv, p. 51c	409
iv, p. 1a	364	iv, p. 18b	465	iv, p. 52a	487
iv, p. 1b	497	iv, p. 19a	413	iv, p. 52b	483
iv, p. 1c	438	iv, p. 19b	414	iv, p. 52c	422
iv, p. 2a	459	iv, p. 20a	439	iv, p. 52d	404
iv, p. 2b	460	iv, p. 26	473	iv, p. 53a	484
iv, p. 3	461	iv, p. 27b	421	iv, p. 53b	488
iv, p. 4	462	iv, p. 39a	499	iv, p. 54a	423
iv, p. 5	426	iv, p. 39b	498	iv, p. 54b	403
iv, p. 6a	393	iv, p. 40a	366	iv, p. 55b	524
iv, p. 6b	394	iv, p. 40b	430	iv, p. 56	369
iv, p. 7a	501	iv, p. 41b	428	iv, p. 56 verso	512
iv, p. 7b	502	iv, p. 42a	418	iv, p. 57a	383
iv, p. 8a	478	iv, p. 42b	419	iv, p. 57b	384
iv, p. 8b	463	iv, p. 44a	389	iv, p. 58	475
iv, p. 9a	503	iv, p. 44b	420	iv, p. 59a	510
iv, p. 9b	464	iv, p. 45a	505	iv, p. 59b	511
iv, p. 10a	415	iv, p. 45b	427	iv, p. 60	431
iv, p. 12a	410	iv, p. 46	479	iv, p. 65a	405
iv, p. 12b	411	iv, p. 47a	527	iv, p. 65b	407
iv, p. 13a	416	iv, p. 47b	372	iv, p. 66a	406
iv, p. 13b	514	iv, p. 48a	387	iv, p. 66b	408
iv, p. 13c	448	iv, p. 48b	528	Military Costumes, iv, p. 89	525
iv, p. 14a	412	iv, p. 49	388	v, p. 4 verso	356
iv, p. 14b	490	iv, p. 50a	534	v, p. 15	137ab
iv, p. 15	368	iv, p. 50b	434	Drawings of Princes and Princesses,	
iv, p. 16	466	iv, p. 50c	373	last page	504

INDEX

CONTENTS